DEAN
ALL-COLOUR
activity
BOOK

PACKED WITH AMAZING
PROJECTS AND PASTIMES

DEAN

This edition first published 1994 by
Dean, an imprint of Reed Children's Books Limited,
Michelin House, 81 Fulham Road, London SW3 6RB,
and Auckland, Melbourne, Singapore and Toronto.

Copyright © 1988, 1989, 1990 Reed International Books Limited

ISBN 0 603 55370 2

Some of the material first appeared in the Hamlyn Colourfax series with the titles: Cartoons and
Animation, Dinosaur and Fossil Activity Book, Exploring Nature, Fun with Nature,
Fun with Science, Out and About, Paper Fun, Spies and Codes.

The Publishers would like to thank the following for their kind permission to reproduce
photographs in this book:

Science Photo Library/Nelson Medina 17 top; David Johnson 29 bottom, 50-51;
The Kobal Collection 61; Imperial War Museum 67;
David Mostyn 85; D. Church 87; Liz and Tony Bomford 104; Peter Loughran/Reed International
Publishing107; E.A. Jones/Nature Photographers 108; Bob Gibbons 109; Eric and David Hosking 111;
Liz and Tony Bomford 114, 118; Judy Todd 120; Paul Sterry/Nature Photographers 121
top; N.A. Callow/ Nature Photographers 121 centre; Reed International Publishing 121
bottom; Bob Gibbons 123; G.E. Hyde/Eric and David Hosking 125.

CONTENTS

WHERE DID DINOSAURS COME FROM?

Where did dinosaurs come from and what happened to them? Thousands of millions of years ago, the first kinds of animals appeared in the sea. With the passing of time, some of these animals altered, little by little, in shape, in habits, and in other ways to suit the changes that were taking place in their watery home. Those animals that did not change in ways which better suited their conditions, or those which changed in ways which made them less able to survive, slowly died out. In this way, animals – and plants – have been changing all the time and, of course, they are continuing to do so. We call this process evolution.

Many primitive sea animals resembled the kind of worm-shaped creature, with a mouth and eyes at one end, that you can roll out from modelling clay or plasticine. If you then flatten the tail end into a fin and pull fins out of the sides, you have a model which looks something like the first fishes. But fins are no use for walking on land. If you now make your fins into two pairs of legs and make the tail round again, you have the basic shape of a land animal such as an amphibian or reptile.

Dinosaurs developed from reptiles

Using modelling clay or plasticine, you can make a worm-like creature evolve into an amphibian.

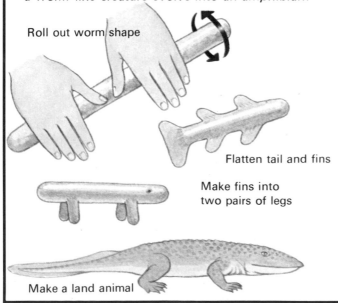

Roll out worm shape

Flatten tail and fins

Make fins into two pairs of legs

Make a land animal

called thecodonts (socket-toothed reptiles), which were sprawling crocodile-like animals that lived and hunted for food mainly in water. Gradually, over the aeons, they changed and many new kinds appeared so that, eventually, dinosaurs were the most successful animals on Earth. But, then, for reasons which are not fully understood, they died out quite suddenly.

GEOLOGICAL TIME SCALE
Scientists believe the Earth is about 4500 million years old, and they break down the history of the Earth into sections with different names. They call this the geological time scale. It shows the different periods of time, with their ages in millions of years.

You can make a mobile, using cut-out dinosaurs, to show when these animals lived in the geological time scale. Shown opposite are some dinosaurs. Trace them on to card and cut them out. Colour them the same colour as the periods on the time scale. For each animal shape cut a piece of thread 15 centimetres (6 inches) long and thread it through the hole in the shape. Now take all the shapes belonging to the Triassic period. (They should all be the same colour.) Attach the free ends of their threads to a piece of wire 30 centimetres (12 inches) long. Now do the same with all the Jurassic animals and all the Cretaceous animals.

Cut another thread about 40 centimetres (16 inches) long and attach it to the wire holding the Triassic animals so that the wire balances when you hold it by the thread. Attach a 30 centimetre (12 inch) thread to the Jurassic wire and allow this to balance, too. Finally, do the same with the Cretaceous wire using a 20 centimetre (8-inch) thread. If you attach the free ends of all these threads to another wire, you can then hang your mobile from the ceiling.

64

— millions of years ago —

Cretaceous

140

Jurassic

200

Triassic

225

Triceratops

Anatosaurus

Tyrannosaurus

Iguanodon

Stegosaurus

Diplodocus

Brachiosaurus

Plateosaurus

Lesothosaurus

finished mobile

Above: *The dinosaurs to use for your mobile*

MODEL DINOSAURS

How do we know what dinosaurs looked like? We only have their skeletons originally in the form of fossilized bones to help us.

If the complete skeleton is preserved, then it is easy to build it up as it was in real life. Scientists sometimes mount them in museums in life-like poses. A display like this is called a **reconstruction**. More often, the bones are taken to the museum in the slab of rock as they are found and put on display just like that.

Trace round the bones that are scattered on this page. You will need to draw some of the bones more than once, so copy them by the number of times indicated. Make holes in the bones where shown. Now you can fix the bones together to make the complete skeleton shown at the bottom of the page. Join the bones with thread. If you wish, you can glue the completed skeleton on to card in a lifelike pose. Then transfer the shapes to stiff card and cut them out.

MAKING A PLASTICINE DINOSAUR
1 mould and soften the plasticine or clay;
2 pull it into the basic shape, making head, body, and tail in one piece; 3 develop the shape but do not add detail to head yet; 4 roll out clay for legs and divide in half; 5 model leg shape before attaching to body, making skin fold; 6 mould legs and arms on to body; 7 shape feet and add claws; 8 using a knife, cut a mouth, bending the head to one side to give movement; 9 bend down jaw to put in teeth; 10 make nostrils, eyelid, and eye with cocktail stick; 11 finally, smooth out all fingernail marks.

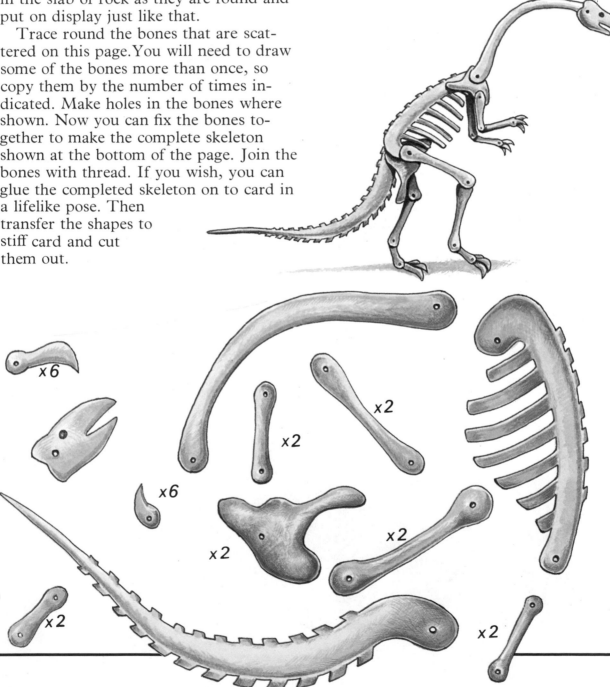

x6

x6

x2

x2

x2

x2

x2

x2

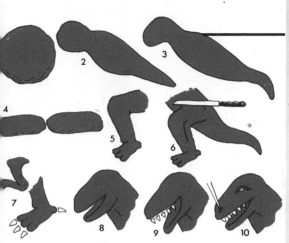

The finished model looks like this – of course you can vary the colours!

MAKING A FRAME DINOSAUR

Making a dinosaur from wire, clingfilm, bandaging, filler glue, toothpicks, and cardboard:

1 Make (A) the body and (B,C,D,E) the legs from wire and cover the shape with clingfilm beginning at the thinnest end (F).

2 Wrap bandaging around the frame, beginning at the thinnest end, so that it overlaps, and glue the ends of the bandage to the body.

3 Mix the filler powder with water into a thick paste, and spread the paste over the body.

4 Cut out cardboard shapes to make the plates on its back. Use pieces of toothpicks for the tail spines. Stick these in before the filler has hardened. Paint your dinosaur.

RESTORING A DINOSAUR

Sometimes it is possible to find complete skeletons of dinosaurs which, even though the bones have become separated, can be

Try restoring any kind of dinosaur following the method shown here.

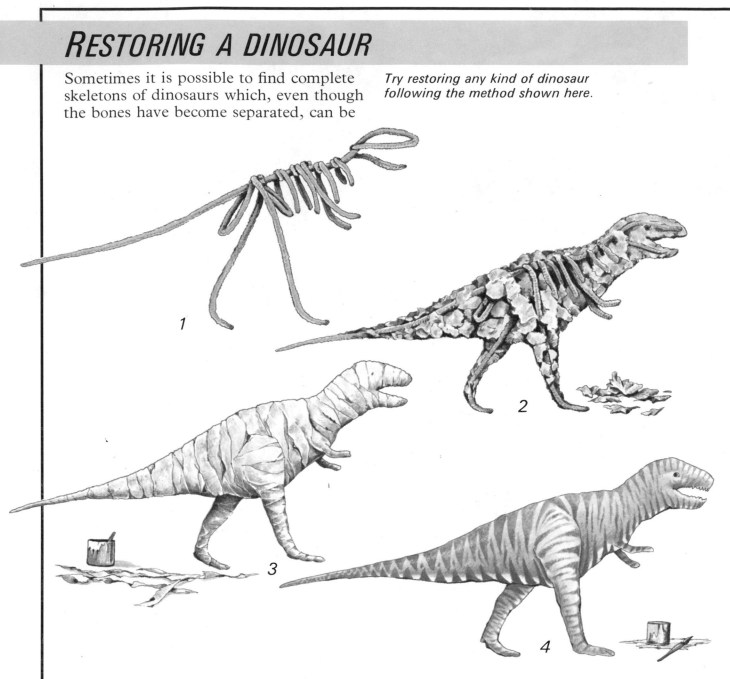

pieced together into a reconstruction. Even if not all the bones are preserved, scientists can make use of the ones they have and then produce a drawing of the whole skeleton.

If you have read other books on dinosaurs, you may have wondered how we are able to suggest what the whole animal looked like. In other words, how do scientists put flesh on the bones to make what is known as a **restoration**? By looking at marks on individual dinosaur bones, a

scientist can decide where the animal's muscles were attached. From this, he or she can build up a picture of the flesh of the animal. Of course, knowing about the anatomy of modern animals helps in this. Then the scientist can guess at what the skin was like and even what colour the animal might have been. Often the scientist then asks a skilled artist to draw an impression of the dinosaur. Sometimes, artists make models of the animals instead. You can do this yourself (*see* above).

Take some pipe cleaners (1) and build a model of one of the dinosaur skeletons on pages 8–15. Twist several pipe cleaners together to make the backbone strong. Now cover it with muscles made from papier mâché (2). Mix some cold-water wallpaper paste and tear some newspaper into strips. Coat the paper strips with paste and wind them around the bones (3) until you build up a good thickness, especially around the legs, neck, and tail. You do not need to fill the space between the ribs with papier mâché. There would be no flesh here, but you can imagine that this is where the lungs, the heart, the intestines, and all the other organs would be. You could make the insides out of coloured modelling clay but, of course, you will not see them when your model is finished.

Wait for your first layer of papier mâché – the flesh layer – to dry. Then tear some small pieces of newspaper, paste them, and cover the whole model to produce a smooth layer of "skin". Make eyes from small beads and, if your animal is a meat eater, make teeth from stiff paper or matchsticks. If it is armoured, cut the armour pieces from stiff card.

When it is dry, paint your animal (4) with poster paints. Try to imagine the colour it would have been. For example, a very big animal could have drab colours. A small animal might be quite bright. Compare a little lizard with a crocodile. Fierce, hunting animals might have been striped or spotted like tigers or leopards. Plant-eating animals might have been camouflaged like modern deer. Any big frills or crests might be brightly coloured so that they can be used as signals, like the bright colours of a modern peacock.

It is not always easy to make a restoration of an animal from a reconstruction of its skeleton. Here is the skeleton of an animal. From what you see, try to draw a restoration of what the animal might have looked like.

A DINOSAUR LANDSCAPE

Fill a shallow wooden tray (about the size of a tea tray) with sand to resemble a desert. You can make a "waterhole" by cutting out from aluminium foil a roughly circular shape. Some small pebbles and bits of grass could make rocks and shrubs around the pond.

Now you need to give your scene a backdrop. Cut out a rectangle of card to fit the back of your tray as shown in the diagram on the right. Fold it in two places so that it can be shaped around the sides of the tray, too. Paint the card with the scene shown here but without the dinosaurs. Fold the backdrop around the tray. You now have your dinosaur landscape and you just need some dinosaurs.

Simply, draw a graph of evenly sized squares (of the right proportion to fit your scene) and copy the dinosaurs square by square. Cut them out leaving tabs at the bottom to push into the sand, and paint them to make them look realistic. Instead, you can just trace out the dinosaurs in the top picture.

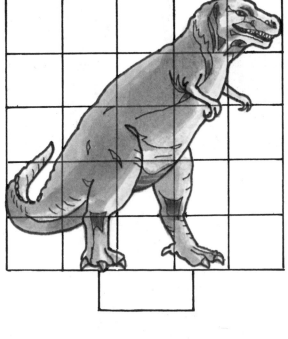

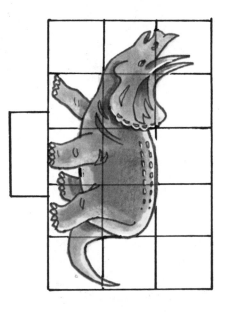

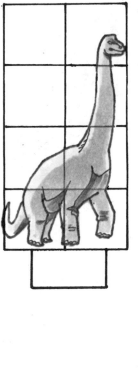

TEST YOUR SENSES

We have five senses in all. They include touch, sight, smell, taste and hearing. Below are some experiments to demonstrate just a few of these.

TAKING FINGERPRINTS

You will need: pencil • paper

Scribble heavily on some paper with a pencil to make a black mark. Rub your finger on it until it is quite black and then press it on to a piece of transparent sticky tape. The ridges that are on the outer layer of skin on your fingers will show up as a fingerprint. Turn the tape over and stick it to a piece of white paper to protect the print.

MAP YOUR TONGUE

You will need: salt • sugar • lemon juice • coffee • mirror • paper • pencil

Small organs, called taste buds, are located just below the surface of the tongue and at three places in the throat. Taste sensations can be divided into sweet, salty, sour and bitter.

Place a small amount of salt (salty taste), sugar (sweet), lemon juice (sour) and coffee (bitter) into separate saucers. Add a small amount of water to each. Now draw an outline like the one below to represent your tongue.

Look in the mirror. Dip a teaspoon in the first solution and place it on any part of your tongue. Mark on the drawing SA to show where you can taste salty. Do it again on another part of your tongue. Do the same thing for the remaining solutions. Use the letters SW for sweet, SO for sour, and BI for bitter. Don't forget to rinse your mouth out between each taste.

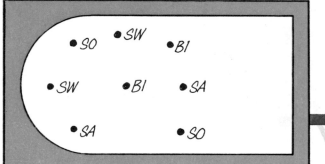

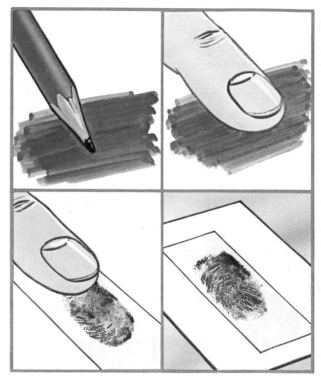

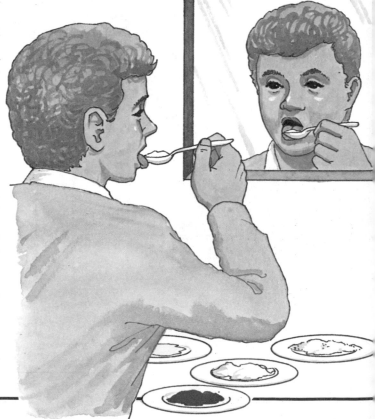

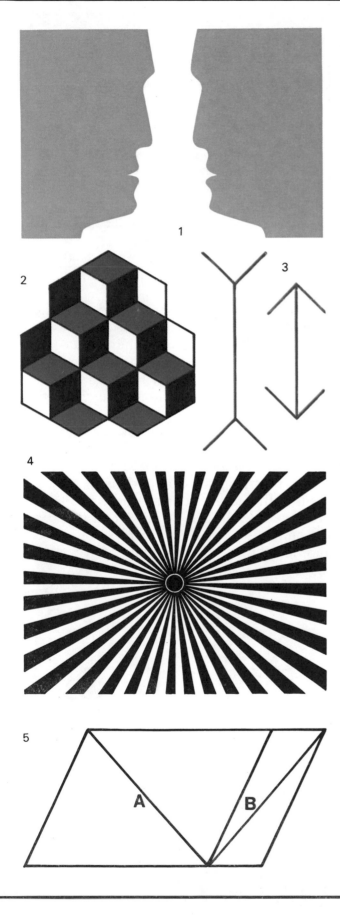

OPTICAL ILLUSIONS

Sometimes our eyes deceive us and things are not what they appear to be. Optical illusions are caused by several things. Sometimes our eyes do not look at an object properly and our brain receives misleading information. Sometimes the brain receives new information and does not know how to interpret it.

For example, can you see two heads or a candlestick in this picture (**1**)? Are the black surfaces the bottom or the top of the cubes (**2**)? Which line is the longer (**3**) and is the pattern moving in **4**? Finally, is A longer than B (**5**)? Try some of these out on your friends.

GETTING ON YOUR NERVES

Ask someone to blindfold you and then press the point of one, two and three pencils in turn, first on your hand and then on the back of your neck. How many pencils can you feel? What do you feel if someone touches the back of your neck with a feather?

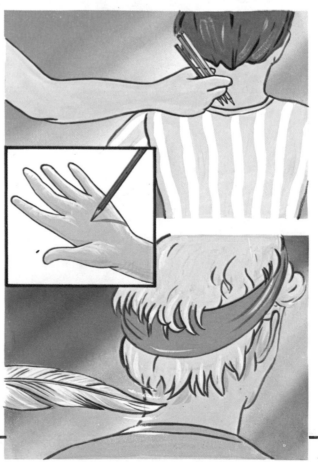

15

INVISIBLE INFLUENCE

You will need: comb ● bits of paper ● balloons

Can you bend water? It might sound impossible, but it isn't. You can do it by using, of all things, your hair.

Comb your hair vigorously for a few seconds and move the comb near to a thin stream of water running from a tap. You will see the water bend because it is attracted by the comb. The comb can also be made to attract other things. Tiny pieces of paper, for example, can be made to jump up to it.

The comb attracts the water and paper because rubbing against your hair has made it electric. We say that it has been given an electric charge. This charge (negative) sets up an opposite electric charge (positive) in the water and paper.

ATTRACTION AND REPULSION

The basic rule for static electricity is that unlike (different) charges attract, and like (the same) charges repel one another. A positive charge and a negative charge will therefore attract each other. But two positive or two negative charges will always repel one another.

The charges attract one another, so that the water bends and the bits of paper jump.

The kind of electricity produced by the comb is called static electricity. It doesn't flow through wires like ordinary electricity. You can give other materials a static electrical charge by rubbing them against wool or fur. Balloons are charged when they are rubbed against your sweater. In this state they can stick to the walls or ceiling.

Charged balloons do not always attract. Tie some string to two balloons. Rub them both against your sweater, and then hold them up by the strings. You will see the balloons push apart, or repel one another. This is because they both have the same electric charge.

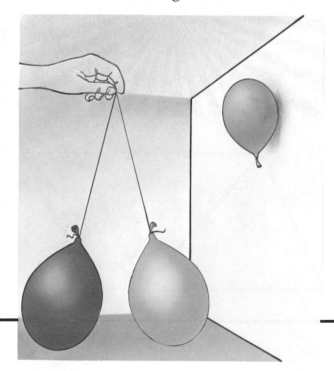

16

JUST FOR THE RECORD

You will need: old LP ● glass ● cloth ● silver foil

A long-playing disc (LP) can be charged with static electricity by rubbing it vigorously with a woollen cloth. Place it on a glass. The glass will act as an insulator and stop the static electricity on the disc leaking away. Throw a few crumpled pieces of silver foil on to the disc (the little silver balls used to decorate cakes will work just as well).

The balls will start dancing about all over the disc. This happens because they become electrically charged themselves as they touch the disc. And because they have the same electric charge, they repel one another. That is what sets them moving.

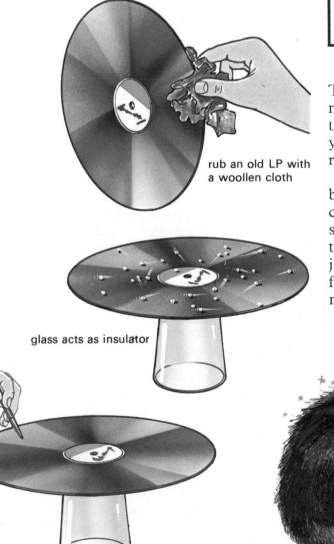

rub an old LP with a woollen cloth

glass acts as insulator

OVERCHARGED

The violent movements of the air, water drops and ice particles in thunderclouds sets up static electricity. This can build up to a very high voltage (pressure), often millions of volts. When this happens, the clouds are no longer able to hold the electricity. It escapes and zig-zags down to the ground in a white-hot flash. This is lightning. The air along the flash expands suddenly with a bang as it is heated. This is the noise we hear as thunder.

You can control the balls leaping about. Try holding a plastic pen and a comb near the balls. What happens? Charge up the pen and comb by rubbing them on your hair or sweater. How do the balls react now?

Your pet cat (if you have one) can also be charged with static electricity. In a cool, dark room gently rub its fur for several minutes, always in the same direction. You will see sparks of electricity jump from the coat and you may hear the fur crackle, too. But your cat will feel nothing.

Magic boats

You will need: balsa wood • nail • paper • straw • plastic tray • magnet • cardboard • soap

These boats all work extremely well. You can make a sailing boat that can sail when there is no wind; a launch driven by soap and a jet-propelled speedboat.

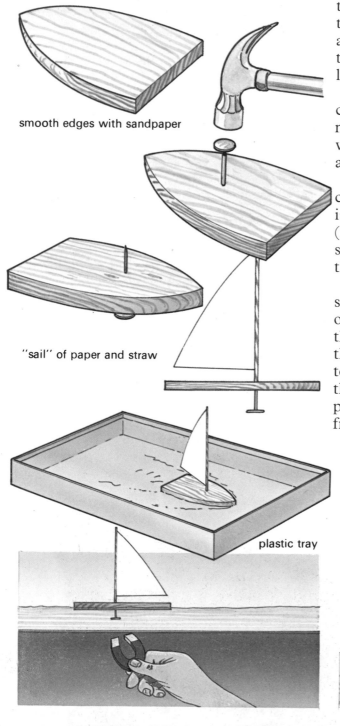

smooth edges with sandpaper

"sail" of paper and straw

plastic tray

Make a small sailing boat by carefully sawing a thin piece of wood into a suitable shape. Ask an adult to help if you are unsteady with a saw. Smooth the edges with sandpaper. Hammer a flat-headed nail (such as a plasterboard nail) through the wood, as shown. Stick a triangular piece of paper onto a straw, and slip the straw over the sharp end of the nail. Your boat is now ready for launching.

Fill a plastic tray with water. You can control your boat by moving a strong magnet underneath the tray. The magnet will attract the nail head under the water and drag the boat along.

Your launch can be made from thick cardboard or plastic foam packing. Wood is too heavy. Cut a notch in the stern (rear) of the launch, and wedge into it a small piece of soap. Place your launch in the water, and it will speed away.

The boat is not really propelled by the soap. The forces that exist on the surface of the water, known as surface tension, do the work. They act, or pull, around anything floating on water. The soap's job is to reduce the surface tension at the rear of the boat, which stops the surface forces pulling there. Those forces working at the front win, dragging the boat along.

small piece of soap

STEAM POWER (X)

You will need: old cigar tube • balsa wood • nail • stiff wire • candle

Your jet-propelled speedboat will be driven by a jet of steam which you will be able to make in a boiler. For this you can use a metal tube (such as a cigar tube) or a small tin with a tight-fitting lid. Use a nail to pierce a small hole in one end of the tube (or tin). Saw a piece of wood into the shape of a boat hull and make a hole near each corner.

Make a four-legged cradle for the tube out of stiff wire. Wind the wire around both ends of the tube, and push the feet into the holes in the wood. Half fill the tube with water and fit the lid on tightly. Place a candle underneath the tube, and light it. Now launch the boat on the water, taking care not to touch the tube, which will be getting hot.

The water in the tube will soon start to boil, and a jet of steam will spurt out of the hole. As the steam escapes backwards, your speedboat will shoot forwards. It will carry on travelling until it runs out of steam.

make a cradle from stiff wire

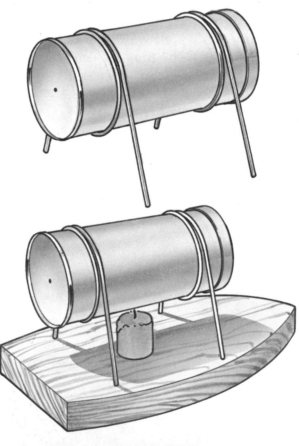

pierce the tube with a nail

tube will get hot – don't touch!

ACTION-REACTION

The jet-propelled speedboat works according to the law of reaction. The force (action) of the steam going backwards, sets up an equal force (reaction) going forwards, and it is this force that propels the boat. Jet planes and space rockets work on exactly the same principle.

MAGNET MAGIC

You will need: 2 bar magnets • cardboard box • lolly sticks • iron filings • compass

Playing with magnets can be lots of fun, and you can learn about the laws of magnetism at the same time. You can buy small bar (straight) magnets or horseshoe magnets, but bar magnets are best for these activities. You will need two.

Hang up each magnet in turn from a piece of thread. Let them come to rest. You will find that both magnets end up pointing in the same direction. If you check with a compass, you will find they point North–South.
Mark N or S on the ends of each magnet according to which way they point.

Place one of the magnets on top of a cardboard box. Draw around it with a pencil and stick ice lolly sticks along the line. Place the magnets in the middle so that the two N ends and the two S ends of the magnets are together. Watch how the top magnet floats in the air!

This shows you that two N ends and two S ends of magnets repel, or push against each other. If you place the top magnet the other way round, the two magnets will stick together. The N and S ends of two magnets attract each other.

You can find out something else about magnets using iron filings. These are tiny specks of iron, which you should be able to buy from a hardware store or hobby shop. Sprinkle a few filings onto your magnet. You will find that they stick only to the ends, not to the middle. This shows that the magnetism is concentrated near the ends, at the "poles" of the magnet.

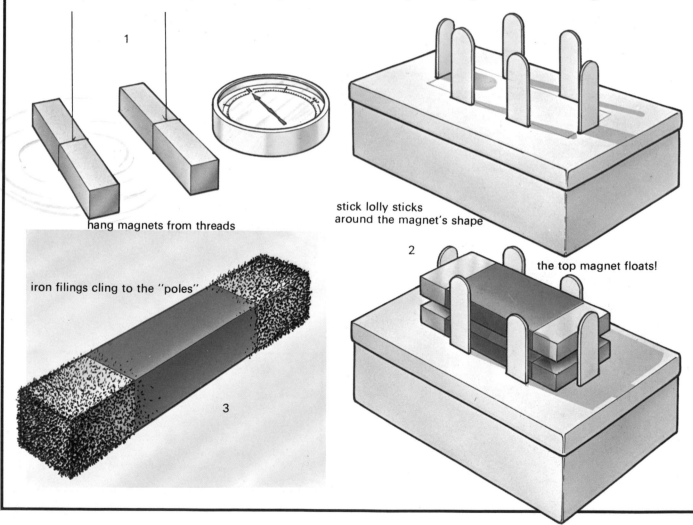

1

hang magnets from threads

stick lolly sticks around the magnet's shape

iron filings cling to the "poles"

3

2

the top magnet floats!

20

MAKING FACES

You will need: card ● copper wire ● tape ● iron filings ● battery

On a piece of card, draw the outline of a face, and then follow the line with a length of copper wire. Tape it in position. Cover the wire with a piece of thin card, and sprinkle some iron filings on top. Connect the ends of the wire to a battery (NOT THE MAINS) and tap the card lightly. The face will suddenly appear.

This happens because when electric current flows in a wire, it creates magnetism. It sets up a magnetic field. The face appears because the iron filings are attracted to the magnetic field around the wire.

This connection between electric current and magnetism is very important. As a result we can make electric motors and electromagnets.

SWITCH-ON POWER

You will need: copper wire ● bolt ● battery ● switch ● paper clips

You can make an electric-current magnet using a length of copper wire and a large nail (or bolt). Wind the wire around the nail many times and tape it in place. Join the ends of the wire to the terminals of a battery through a simple switch (*see page 22*). Switch on. Bring the nail head near some paper clips and drawing pins, and watch them jump to it. Switch off the current, and the pins and clips will fall away.

By winding the wire in a coil around the nail, you have made it into a magnet when the current is flowing. But the magnetism goes when the current is switched off. We call such a magnet an electromagnet.

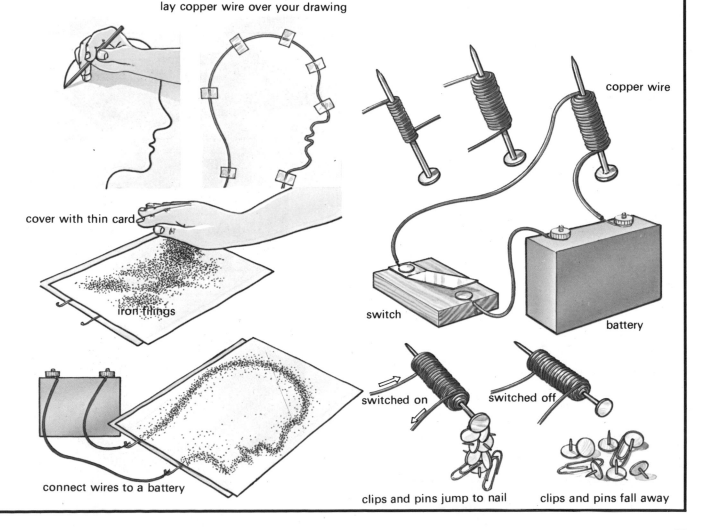

lay copper wire over your drawing

cover with thin card

iron filings

connect wires to a battery

copper wire

switch

battery

switched on

switched off

clips and pins jump to nail

clips and pins fall away

21

MORSE CODE

You will need: wood • drawing pins • copper wire • tin can • 9-volt lantern battery

Today we live in an age of instant communications. You can talk on the phone to friends in distant places. You can hear on the radio and see on the TV things happening on the other side of the world.

Until about 150 years ago there were no means of instant communications. The quickest way to send a message was by horse rider. Then, in the 1830s, Samuel Morse in the United States invented an electric telegraph. He sent messages along wires using electricity.

You can make an electric telegraph yourself with simple apparatus – pieces of wood, a few drawing pins, a long length of copper wire, two strips from a tin can and a battery. Try to use bell wire – you should be able to buy it at a hardware store or electrical shop. For the battery, use a 9-volt lantern battery or something similar.

You need to make two kinds of devices – a sender, or key, to transmit messages; and a receiver, or sounder, to receive them. Make the sender using a strip cut from a tin can. Cut it out carefully with tin snips, or ask an adult to do it for you. Pin the strip in position, as shown in the picture, but don't push the drawing pins fully in yet.

To make the receiver, nail two pieces of wood together into an L-shape, as shown. Hammer a nail into the base and wind round it about 40 turns of wire. Tape it in position. Fix another tin strip on the upright piece of wood so that one end is a few millimetres above the head of the nail.

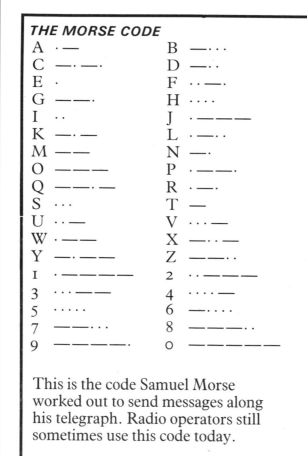

THE MORSE CODE

A	· —	B	— · · ·
C	— · — ·	D	— · ·
E	·	F	· · — ·
G	— — ·	H	· · · ·
I	· ·	J	· — — —
K	— · —	L	· — · ·
M	— —	N	— ·
O	— — —	P	· — — ·
Q	— — · —	R	· — ·
S	· · ·	T	—
U	· · —	V	· · · —
W	· — —	X	— · · —
Y	— · — —	Z	— — · ·
1	· — — — —	2	· · — — —
3	· · · — —	4	· · · · —
5	· · · · ·	6	— · · · ·
7	— — · · ·	8	— — — · ·
9	— — — — ·	0	— — — — —

This is the code Samuel Morse worked out to send messages along his telegraph. Radio operators still sometimes use this code today.

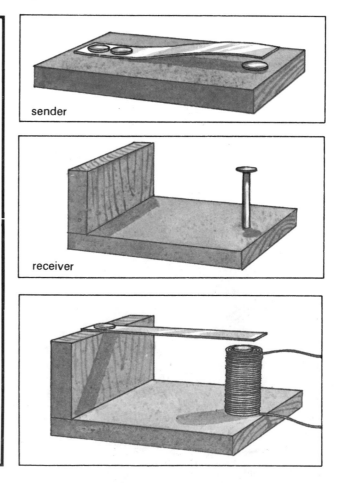

sender

receiver

Join one end of the wire from the coil to the fixed end of the sender, and the other to one terminal of the battery. Join the other battery terminal to the drawing pin beneath the free end of the sender strip, as in the picture.

Now you can send your message by tapping the sender. When you press down, the strip makes contact with the drawing pin underneath, and this completes the electrical circuit between the battery and the coil in the receiver. Current flows through the coil and turns the nail into an electromagnet (*see page 21*.) The nail then attracts the strip above it, making a "click". When the sender is released, current stops flowing, and the nail stops being magnetic. The strip in the receiver springs away. You use these clicks to send messages in the Morse code, clicking quickly for dots, and slowly for dashes.

THE MODERN TELEGRAPH

The modern version of Morse's electric telegraph is the telex, now widely used in businesses throughout the world.

Messages are sent from one subscriber to another by code (but not Morse code), using machines called teleprinters. A person sending a message types it on a typewriter-like keyboard. The teleprinter changes the message into coded electric signals and transmits them to the receiving teleprinter. This changes the coded signals back into words, and types them out to give a printed message.

Pictures, too, can be transmitted along communications lines, using fax, or facsimile machines. The fax transmitter changes a picture into coded electric signals, and the receiver changes them back into a picture again.

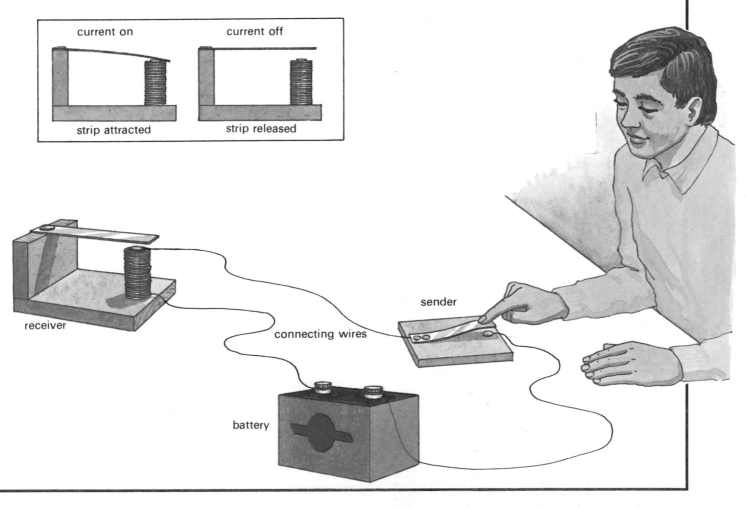

current on   current off

strip attracted   strip released

receiver

connecting wires

sender

battery

SPREADING COLOURS

You will need: blotting paper • coloured ink • 2 glass jars • card

If you enjoy painting, you will know that you can make new colours by mixing together different coloured paints. For example, you can make green by mixing together yellow and blue. In the same way you can make new colours by mixing together different coloured inks. In fact most of the inks in bottles and in felt-tip pens are mixtures of different coloured dyes. You can find out which in this experiment.

Take a strip of blotting paper, and drip a few drops of, for example, black ink near one end. Suspend the paper from a pencil so that this end dips into water in the bottom of a jar. Make sure the ink spot is above the water level.

The water will slowly rise through the blotting paper and through the ink spot. Gradually, different colours start appearing above the spot. These are the different coloured dyes that were mixed together to make the black ink.

COLOUR SEPARATING

This method of separating colours is known as chromatography, which means "colour drawing". Chemists often use it in chemical analysis, to find what substances are present in a sample of something. They may use paper chromatography, like you do, or perform the experiment in a tube packed with suitable material. They may then pass special liquids or gases through the tube. Gas chromatography can detect the very tiniest traces of substances imaginable.

A COLOUR FOUNTAIN

You will need: jar of hot water • jar of cold water • coloured ink • card

This is a dramatic way to see colours spreading.

Fill a glass jar with hot water and add a few drops of coloured ink. Fill a second jar with cold water and, holding a piece of card over the top, carefully turn the jar upside down and place it on top of the first one. Remove the card. You will see a spectacular fountain of colour as the hot water rises into the top jar.

THE SPECTRUM

The band of colours in a rainbow is called a spectrum. You can produce a spectrum in other ways. A good way is to pass sunlight through a wedge-shaped piece of glass, known as a prism. The colours spread out as they enter and leave the faces of the glass. They do this because different colours bend by different amounts when they pass through a surface. Violet light is bent the most, red light the least.

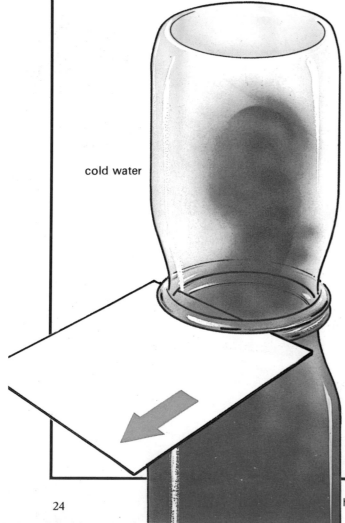

cold water

hot coloured water

VANISHING COLOURS

You will need: card • protractor • crayons •
nail • glue

You have seen how you can split up white
light into a rainbow of colours. You can
also do the reverse – turn the colours of
the rainbow back into white light.

Cut out a disc from a piece of card and
divide it up into six equal parts. Use a
protractor to do this, measuring an angle
of 60 degrees for each segment. Colour
the segments in the order in which they
appear in the rainbow – red, orange,
yellow, green, blue and violet.

Push a flat-headed nail (such as a plasterboard nail) through the middle of the
disc and glue it in place. When the glue
has set, fix the nail in the head of a hand
drill and turn the handle. As the disc
spins faster and faster, the colours blend
together to make white.

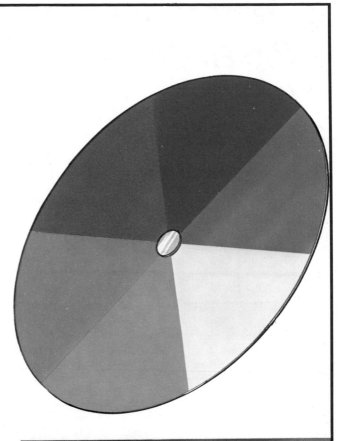

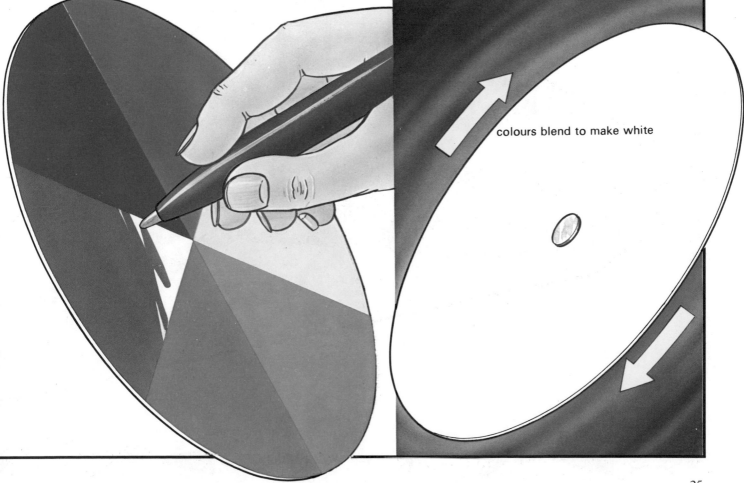

colours blend to make white

25

PAPER ON THE MOVE

FOLDED GLIDERS

You will need: 2 rectangular pieces of paper about 20 cm by 30 cm

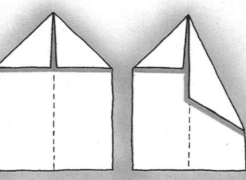

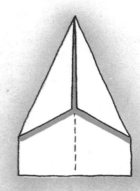

1 Fold one piece of paper in half lengthways to mark the centre. Unfold it and lay it flat, with the centre crease running directly away from you.

2 Fold the top right corner down to the centre line and crease it well. Do the same with the top left corner.

3 Now fold the right edge to the centre line, then do the same for the left side.

4 Crease both the folds well.

You can give your glider bigger wings to help it fly even better. Take a similar piece of paper and repeat steps 1 to 4. Slide your glider inside, under the flaps of the second sheet until the tip is snugly in place.

You can fasten the two sections together with a little glue, then gently throw the glider high into the air for long distance flying.

5 *Fold the paper in half along the centre line so that the flaps are inside.*

6 *Fold each side back, again lengthways, about 15 mm from the centre fold. The glider is now ready to fly.*

FINGER PROPELLER

You will need: A sheet of paper 7.5 cm by 15 cm. Make sure the paper size and folds are exact

1 *Make folds along all 4 sides of the paper about 6 mm from the edge.*

2 *Where the folds cross at the corners, flatten them a little more and pinch the corners upwards and outwards to form sharp points. It should look like a shallow dish with very pointed corners.*

To make your finger propeller spin, hold the paper between the tips of your index fingers. Your right finger should be on the centre of the flat side and your left finger should be on the centre of the side with the points.

With plenty of room for a straight run, turn your back to the direction you intend to run in. Still holding the paper between your fingertips, point your right index straight ahead. Turn around quickly but smoothly and start running. Remove your left finger and the propeller will spin on the end of your right finger as you run.

PAPIER-MÂCHÉ

Papier-mâché is quite messy to work with so you will need plenty of room. Choose somewhere where no-one will mind a mess and place a waterproof covering on the floor or table. The paste takes several hours to dry between layers, so you will need to be able to leave your work out where it won't be in anyone's way.

Tearing paper
Paper has a grain like wood. Tearing and folding along the grain is neater and easier than across the grain. Tear some old newspapers into fairly even strips about 2 cm wide and no longer than 12–15 cm long. Longer strips are harder to work with. Final layers will require even narrower strips.

Mixing paste
Wallpaper paste is best and you can buy this in small quantities. Mix according to the instructions and only make a small batch at a time as it does not keep for long. You can make your own paste from flour and water, but it can sometimes go mouldy.

Building up layers
Papier-mâché is a means of building up overlapping layers of paper soaked in paste. When the paste dries, the paper hardens. Build up the layers carefully, keeping to the planned shape of what you are making. Make sure that each layer is completely dry before starting the next. A layer should not be more than three or four sheets of paper thick.

After removing the paper from the paste, draw it gently between two fingers of one hand to clean off surplus paste. Smooth the pasted strip onto your model without leaving air bubbles or creases.

HOT-AIR BALLOON

You will need: Papier-mâché • balloon • paints or coloured markers • thin string • a small plastic pot or yoghurt carton • coloured paper

1 *Blow up the balloon to the size you want. Starting at the opposite end to the nozzle, apply the strips of papier-mâché until all the balloon has been evenly covered, leaving a circle about 5–7.5 cm in diameter at the nozzle end.*

2 *When it is dry, add another layer and repeat until the fourth or fifth layer. Take special care to make the last layer as smooth as possible. Once this is dry, pop the balloon and remove it. Carefully lay more strips around the opening to build up a neat finish.*

3 *Use short strips of papier-mâché to fix a rubber band to the end opposite the opening.*

SPACE HELMET

You will need: Papier-mâché ● large balloon ● large piece of thin card ● sticky tape ● 2 yoghurt pots ● paints or markers

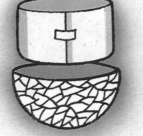

1 Blow up the balloon until it is larger than your head and apply a layer of papier-mâché until half way up the balloon. When dry, add another layer and repeat for 4 layers.

2 When the final layer is dry, cut a strip of thin card about 25 cm wide and long enough to fit loosely around your head. Tape it into a tube. Pop the balloon and remove it from the papier-mâché.

3 Insert the card tube and tape into position as shown. Cover with papier-mâché to match the part already made.

4 Ask your parents to cut a large square opening in one side. Cover the yoghurt pots with papier-mâché then use papier-mâché strips to fix a yoghurt pot to each side of the opening and paint the helmet.

4 While this is drying, glue coloured paper to the plastic pot. Taking great care, use a skewer or the point of a pair of scissors to make 4 holes at equal distances in the rim.

5 Cut 4 pieces of string 10 cm long and tie a simple knot in the end of each. Thread one through each of the holes in the pot from the inside.

6 When the papier-mâché globe is completely dry, make 4 holes in the rim of the opening at equal distances.

Thread the pieces of string through from the outside and tie a knot in the end of each, making sure that the pot hangs level. You can now decorate the outside of your hot-air balloon.

POP-UP CARDS

If you are going to post your card, make it to fit a standard size envelope. Huge or strangely shaped home-made envelopes may mean extra postage!

A greetings card opens from the right like a book or from the bottom. It can be of single thickness with one fold, or double thickness with two folds. There are different ways of doing pop-up cards. Something can pop up from the top, out of the centre fold or a part can be moved with a tab.

HALLOWEEN CARD WITH BAT

You will need: Heavy paper 10 cm × 20 cm ● lightweight paper ● coloured markers ● glue

1 *Trace the bat pattern onto the heavy paper and fold the paper in half the short way.*

2 *Cut out the bat and crease the centre fold firmly. Following the dotted lines shown, fold the bat's wings forward and then back,* *then forward again. Vary the angle of the folds as shown, keeping the bat as symmetrical as possible.*

3 *Use bright colours for the eyes and background. Draw a scary background, perhaps with a bright moon and a spooky castle.*

4 *Fold the card and fold the bat, then slip the bat into the closed card to find the right position. Hold the wing tips in place with* *your thumbs as you open the card. Glue the wing tips in place. Now you can write your message.*

BIRTHDAY CARD

You will need: Heavy paper • lightweight paper • glue

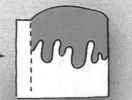

1 Start with paper that is twice as big as the card will be. Fold it in half one way, then in half again the other way.

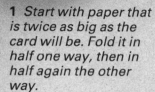

3 Stick the tab to the middle of the card. Stick decorations and candles on the cake. Cut a pull tab 12 mm wide and long enough to reach from the cake to beyond the side of the card.

2 Cut out a cake shape from the lightweight paper. It should be a little less than half as wide as the part of the card you will glue it to. Allow enough paper for a tab about 6 mm wide and almost as high as the cake along the left of the cake.

CUT

4 Flip the cake over to face the right way and mark where its right edge touches the card. Flip it onto the wrong side. Unfold the card and cut a 12 mm vertical slit in the top layer 12 mm to the left of this mark.

5 Slip the pull tab through the slit and out between the layers of paper. Fold over the end of the tab inside the card and carefully glue to the back of the cake.

Flip the cake to the left and trim the outside end of the tab to 12 mm. Write 'PULL' on the end and finish your card.

ROLLING EYES CARD

You will need: Heavy paper • paper fastener • marker pens

1 Make the double fold as shown.

2 Mark the card where you want the face to be and open the card again. Draw the face or cut one from paper and stick it in place. Leave out the eyes.

3 Cut 2 holes for the eyes and poke a tiny hole through the nose. Cut a circle of paper about the same size as the head and make a tiny hole in the centre.

Pass the paper fastener through the holes in the card and the paper circle. Bend the prongs so that the circle turns freely. Draw the eyes through the eye holes onto the paper circle.

4 Cut a strip of paper about 12 mm wide and long enough to reach from the circle to outside the card. Glue one end to the circle and draw an arrow on the other to show how to work it.

TRICKS AND PUZZLES

MOBIUS TRICK STRIP

You will need: Lightweight paper ● pencil ● scissors ● glue

Cut a strip of paper about 3 cm wide and 30 cm long. Bring the 2 ends together, twisting *one* of them over before gluing them to each other. You will now have a twisted loop of paper.

You can prove that your trick strip only has ONE side, not 2 like ordinary paper! Just draw a line along the strip without lifting the pencil from the paper. You will come back to the beginning of the lines, but although you never turned the paper over, the line will be on both sides!

Now cut along the line with scissors. When you reach the start of your cut the loop should fall into two pieces. But it doesn't! It makes one bigger loop instead.

Make another trick strip, but this time make your cut 5 mm from one edge. You will eventually pass the beginning of your cut on the other side of the strip. Stop when you meet it again. You will be surprised to see that you now have one loop of paper passing through another!

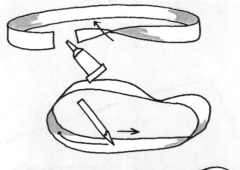

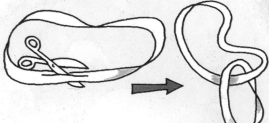

INSIDE-OUT CUBE

You will need: Paper ● tape ● glue ● pencil and coloured markers

1 Cut a strip of paper 5 cm wide and 40 cm long. Mark the strip in 5 cm squares and number them 1 to 8 from left to right on both *sides. Each* square must have the same number on each side. Draw a line along both edges of each end of the strip.

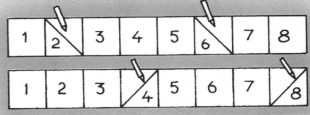

2 With the numbered squares running left to right, draw a diagonal line from the top left corner to the bottom right corner of squares 2 and 6. Flip the strip over and draw in diagonals from top right to bottom left on squares 4 and 8.

3 Flip the strip back to the first side again. Fold the strip towards you along the diagonal you drew on squares 2 and 6. Fold the strip away from you along the diagonal on squares 4 and 8. Carefully open each of the triangles you have made to glue them down. You will now have a strip of 4 squares and 4 triangles.

4 Colour one side of the strip and lay it in front of you coloured side down, with the square numbered 1 on the left.

32

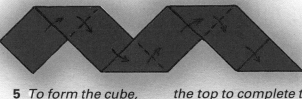

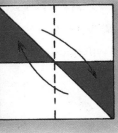

5 To form the cube, fold each of the squares and triangles from left to right, at right angles to the next shape. Continue until you fold triangle 8 over the top to complete the cube. The 2 marked ends should meet. Tape them together edge to edge.

6 To turn your cube inside out, place the cube on the table with a side with a diagonal opening running towards and away from you. Gently push the right half away from you and down, and the left half towards you and down. The cube will collapse and form a flat square with a corner towards you.

7 Turn the square clockwise so that its nearest side runs from left to right. Fold the top half over to make a rectangle.

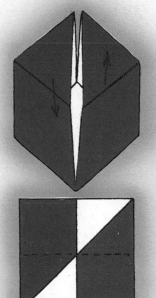

8 Lift the top right corner and open it downwards and towards you to make a white lozenge shape. Hold the top left corner down and fold the right half of the lozenge under the left half to form a rectangle with a short edge towards you.

9 Unfold the top flap of the rectangle, like opening a book, to make a large square again. Turn the square to the right until the diagonal runs towards and away from you once again.

10 Slide the diagonal edges in opposite directions and lift into a cube again. Ease the coloured inside down. The cube will be inside out!

PAPER TREE

Turn a newspaper back into the tree it was made from.

You will need: Newspaper ● scissors ● tape

1 Roll 3 or 4 sheets of newspaper into a tube. Fix with tape in the middle and one end.

2 Make 4 15 cm cuts in the untaped end as shown. Stand tube on end, fold back 4 strips and gently pull inside sections upwards.

33

ORIGAMI

JUMPING FROG

You will need: Lightweight card 5 cm by 8 cm

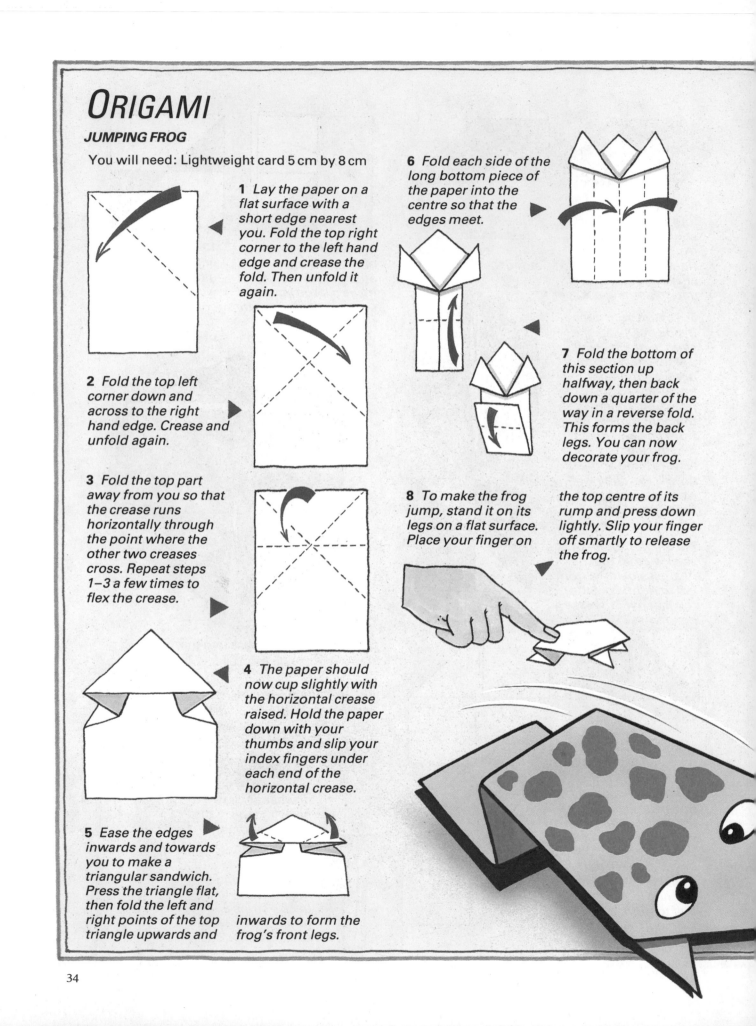

1 Lay the paper on a flat surface with a short edge nearest you. Fold the top right corner to the left hand edge and crease the fold. Then unfold it again.

2 Fold the top left corner down and across to the right hand edge. Crease and unfold again.

3 Fold the top part away from you so that the crease runs horizontally through the point where the other two creases cross. Repeat steps 1–3 a few times to flex the crease.

4 The paper should now cup slightly with the horizontal crease raised. Hold the paper down with your thumbs and slip your index fingers under each end of the horizontal crease.

5 Ease the edges inwards and towards you to make a triangular sandwich. Press the triangle flat, then fold the left and right points of the top triangle upwards and inwards to form the frog's front legs.

6 Fold each side of the long bottom piece of the paper into the centre so that the edges meet.

7 Fold the bottom of this section up halfway, then back down a quarter of the way in a reverse fold. This forms the back legs. You can now decorate your frog.

8 To make the frog jump, stand it on its legs on a flat surface. Place your finger on the top centre of its rump and press down lightly. Slip your finger off smartly to release the frog.

POPPER

You will need: Rectangular piece of lightweight paper

1 Fold the paper lengthways, crease and then unfold.

2 Fold each of the corners in to the centre crease to make a lozenge shape.

3 Fold the lozenge in half lengthways along the centre crease.

4 Fold it in half again the opposite way by bringing the point nearest you up to the furthest point. Unfold again.

7 Fold the upper triangle away from you along the horizontal crease.

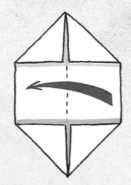

5 Turn the whole shape over away from you so that the points change places and the horizontal crease rises upwards.

6 Fold each point inwards so that their long edges lie along the horizontal crease. You should now have a square divided into 2 triangles.

8 Hold the popper by the 2 free points and snap your hand sharply downwards.

If it doesn't 'pop', loosen the inner folds slightly and try again.

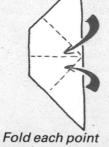

35

ORIGAMI (2)

FLYING CRANE

You will need: A piece of fairly heavy paper
15–20 cm square ● marker pens

1 Fold the paper in half along a diagonal, open it and repeat along the other diagonal.

2 Turn the paper over and fold it in half from side to side. Open it and repeat for the other 2 sides.

3 Place the paper in front of you with a corner pointing towards you and the centre raised. Lightly slide the left and right points towards the centre, and flatten the nearest and furthest squares on top of one another.

4 You should now have a small square. Lay it on the table so that the open-pointed end and the diagonal crease point towards you. Each of the 2 nearest sides consists of 4 layers of paper. Fold up the top 2 on each side to lie along the diagonal crease.

5 Fold the far corner of the square down over the far edges of the 2 triangular flaps you made in step 4.

6 Unfold the step 4 flaps.

7 Hold down all the points facing you and pull just the top point up and away from you.

8 Push in the 2 sides towards the centre to form a long, flat diamond shape and crease. The point nearest you should lie over a small square.

9 Turn the paper over with the same point away from you and the square now on top of the diamond.

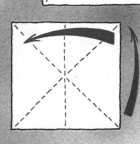

10 Fold the 2 nearest edges of the square in and up to the centre crease as in step 4. Fold the furthest point of the square over these new flaps and open them out again as in steps 5 and 6.

11 Take the top layer of the points facing you, fold it up and away as step 7. Press in the sides and flatten as step 8.

12 You should now have just 2 points nearest to you. Fold

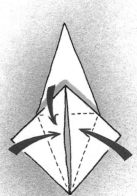

these up and out so that the inner edge lies along the centre horizontal crease to form a 'boat' shape.

13 Unfold them again, turn the diamond over and repeat step 12. Unfold them. Put a pencil mark on the outside edge of each nearest point where the diagonals run from the centre of the diamond.

14 Hold down the left side and push a finger between the two layers of the right point at your mark. Lift your mark up and directly away from you and press it flat.

15 Use your other hand to flatten this shape so it points to the right. Fold the top half of this small diamond over the bottom half and flatten. Do the same for the left side.

16 Pick up the model and press down the tip of the right point and reverse fold it to form the head.

17 Take the nearest of the triangles pointing away from you and fold it lightly towards you and to the right. Turn the 'crane' round and fold the other triangle the same way.

18 Make the crane flap by holding its 'crest' and pulling the tail to and fro.

PAPER ARCHITECTURE

SIMPLE HOUSE

You will need: Heavy paper about 20 cm square ● glue or tape ● scissors ● coloured paper or markers

1 Fold the paper in half from side to side, then in half again the same way. Unfold it.

2 Fold the paper in half from top to bottom, then in half again the same way. It will now be creased into 16 squares. Repeat steps 1 and 2 to loosen folds.

3 With a straight edge towards you, cut along each of the 3 nearest vertical creases to where they meet the first horizontal crease. Repeat on the opposite side.

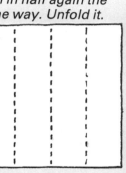

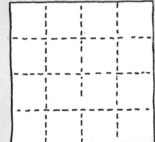

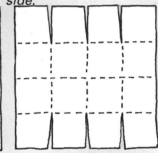

4 Fold the paper between the central flaps on each side so that the flaps cross over each other. Glue them together.

5 To make the walls, fold down the two outer rows of squares so that the end flaps lie across the diagonals of the gable end squares and glue into place. Cut any doors and windows and decorate the walls and roof.

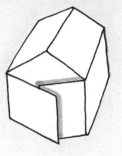

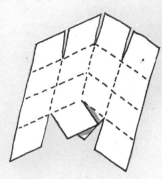

6 To make a chimney, fold a 20 cm by 5 cm piece of paper in half twice to make a 5 cm square. Refold it to make a square tube and glue. Cut a right-angled notch in 2 opposite sides and fix in place.

TOWER AND DRAWBRIDGE

You will need: Heavy paper or light card 20 cm by 40 cm ● tape or glue ● coloured markers

1 Fold the paper in half then again the same way. Open it out to show 4 10 cm by 20 cm rectangles that will be the walls.

2 Lay the paper flat and draw or cut out any doors or windows. Draw on stonework or cut varying small rectangles of brown or grey paper and stick them in place around windows, doors and over the walls. Draw on ivy as well.

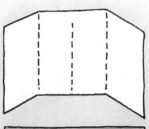

3 Form the tower by folding along the creases into a square tube. Tape securely from the inside.

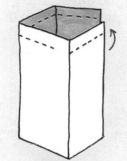

4 Make 1 cm cuts at 1 cm intervals around the top edge of the tower and fold them inwards as shown.

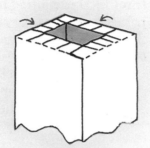

5 Cut a 10 cm square piece of card and glue it to the folded tabs for the roof. Add a trapdoor if desired.

6 Make the battlements from a piece of paper 4 cm by about 42 cm. Make cuts 2 cm deep and 2 cm apart along one long edge.

10 Take 60 cm of thread, push it down through one of the drawbridge holes and up through the other. Push each end through the holes above the door then up through the holes in the roof and tie together. Pull to work the drawbridge.

7 Fold over every other flap to form a right angle. Wrap the strip around the top of the tower, creasing the corners, so that it rests on the tabs. Glue or tape in place.

8 To make a drawbridge, cut a piece of card to the height of the doorway and 2 cm wider. Draw on planks.

9 Pierce 2 small holes in the corners of one end. Tape the other end to the base of the doorway. Make 2 holes above the doorway and 2 in the roof on the same side.

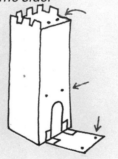

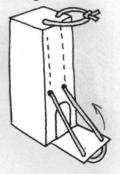

TREE
You will need: Heavy paper ● card ● scissors ● glue ● stapler

1 Cut a piece of paper 15 cm by 21 cm, roll and glue into a tube 2 cm in diameter.

2 Make 4 cuts, 2 cm long, into one end of the tube, and 8 cuts, 3 cm long, into the other end.

3 Use 4 sheets of paper about 15 cm by 20 cm for the leaves. Fold in half and cut out a leafy shape. Lay them together with the creases in line. Staple along the crease.

4 Open out and slot into the 8 slits in the top of the trunk. Glue in place.

5 Glue the roots to a piece of card.

In The Theatre

YOUR OWN THEATRE

You will need: Cardboard box ● scissors ● paper ● paints ● coloured paper

Cut off the flaps of the box – the open end will be the stage front. Cut 3 long strips 2.5 cm wide at each side to work the puppets through. Then cut 2 slits 1.5 cm wide in the top for scenery. It might be easier if you ask your parents to cut these with a sharp knife.

Cut another slit across the top near the front for a curtain. Cut a piece of coloured paper as wide as the slit and 3 cm higher than the box. Simply slide this up and down as a curtain.

Use coloured paper or paint to decorate the stage floor, and cut an arch from a large piece of card to decorate the front of the theatre.

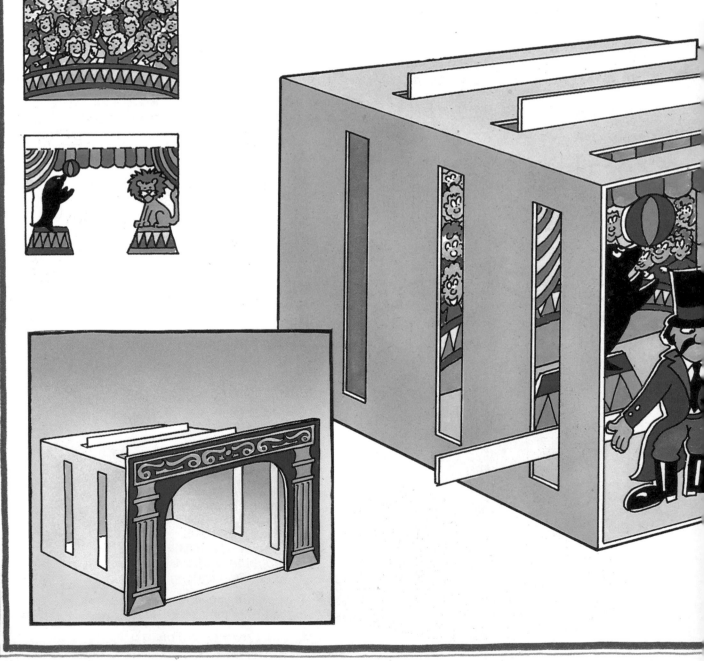

Scenery

Measure the inside size of the stage and cut backdrop scenery from lightweight card. Make it 3 cm higher than the box so that you can lift it out easily. The scenery for the nearest slit to the front should be open in the middle to show the backdrop. You can make spare sets of scenery decorated in different ways to suit your plays.

The play

Decide what play you are going to do before you make your puppets and scenery. Invent your own to tell different stories using the same characters and settings.

When you are deciding on a play, think about who is going to work the puppets so you don't get in a muddle trying to operate too many puppets at once. Remember that you can only work one puppet at a time if they have moving legs.

Hints and tips

If you can stand your theatre on the narrow end of a table top it will give you plenty of room to operate the puppets. Use a cassette recorder to provide music or sound effects for added atmosphere.

Lighting

You can create dramatic effects quite easily by using a portable reading lamp to light the front of the stage. This is especially effective if you darken the room, but make sure it is not in the audience's way. You can make coloured lights by fixing coloured cellophane over a torch and shining it down from the scenery slots.

Sound effects

You can add realism to your plays with some simple sound effects. Two upturned empty yoghurt pots can sound like horses' hooves if you knock them on the table. Crumpling cellophane or empty crisp bags sounds like a roaring fire.

If there is a storm in your play, shake a large piece of stiff card and it can sound like thunder, or trickle uncooked rice onto a baking tray for the sound of rain. A tin with a lid filled with small pebbles sounds like marching feet if you jerk it up and down slowly.

A damp cork rubbed slowly down an empty bottle can imitate squeaky floor boards or door hinges. Experiment with different things to see what other kinds of noises you can imitate.

TRICKS AND MAGIC

LEARNING TO BE A MAGICIAN

Magic is the art of making people believe that you have made something impossible happen. This book will show you how to perform amazing tricks and illusions to fool an audience. If you practise them hard enough you might even become a great magician!

Learn the tricks slowly, step by step, until you can do them perfectly, and practise in front of a mirror to get an audience's view. Some tricks are harder than others, but if you take time to learn them your patience will be rewarded.

Each trick includes suggestions for what to say when you are performing, but you can make up your own 'patter' if you prefer. The idea is to distract attention from what you are really doing and so complete the illusion.

A magician is also an entertainer, so keep your act lively and flowing. If a trick goes wrong, make a joke about the magic not working well today and go on to the next one – don't try it again! Finally, never tell anyone how a trick is done, and never show an audience the same trick twice. Happy conjuring!

THE MAGICIAN'S TABLE

You will need a table on which to perform your tricks. If you can find one with a small drawer in it, that would be ideal. Position the table so that the drawer faces you and keep the drawer slightly open, so you can drop things in it secretly. Line the drawer with a cloth wrapped over a folded sheet of newspaper to deaden the sound.

If you haven't got a table with a drawer, cover any table you can find with a large tablecloth, and pin up the side of the cloth nearest you with two large safety pins. In this way, you will make a large pocket called a *servante*. This is another device for dropping things in without being seen.

THE MAGICIAN'S CLOTHES

Traditionally, magicians wear evening suits with shiny top hats. A good compromise would be to wear a black cloak, which you may be able to borrow, buy, or make from a piece of black cloth. Wear a jacket underneath the cloak, one with pockets and loose sleeves for hiding things in!

MAKING A WAND

Every magician needs a wand. Make one from a piece of stick, such as a garden cane or piece of dowelling about 30 cm long, and paint it black, apart from 3 cm at each end, which you should paint white *after* the black paint has dried.

MAKING A TOP HAT

You will need: thin black card measuring approximately 160 × 130 cm • sticky tape • scissors • pair of compasses and pencil • tape measure

1 Measure round your head, then cut out a rectangle of card the length of this measurement along one edge and 22 cm along the other edge. Draw a pencil line 2 cm from the end of the 22 cm edge and make small cuts from the bottom of the card to the 2 cm line. Now fold the rectangle round to make

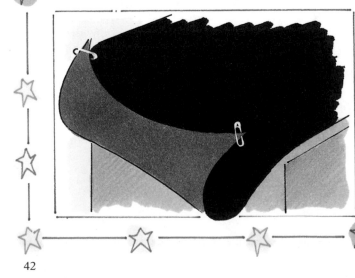

42

the crown of your hat. Stick it together on the inside with tape.

2 Now measure across the crown of the hat, making sure that your tape measure goes through the exact centre. Set your compasses to half this measurement and draw a circle of this size on the remaining card. Then draw another circle 2 cm wider. Cut out the larger circle and cut small 'teeth' all the way round it to the smaller circle. This will be the top of your hat.

3 Now draw another two circles of card, one inside the other. The inner circle's diameter should be very slightly larger than the diameter of the top of the hat, the outer circle 8 cm larger than the inner. Cut out the outer and then the inner circle leaving a ring which forms the brim of the hat.

4 Now the hat is ready to be assembled. Take the top of the hat and bend the cut pieces down. Then put the top onto the uncut edge of the crown with the cut pieces inside. Stick the pieces down with tape.

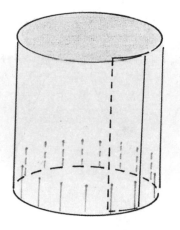

5 Finally, slide the brim over the crown until it reaches the cut end. Bend the cut pieces of the crown upwards and tape them underneath the brim.

And hey presto, your top hat is ready!

COINING IT

PALMING

The secret of coin tricks, and other tricks in which small objects disappear and then reappear, is 'palming', that is hiding an object in your hand. It is best to practise with a small coin, especially if your hands are not very big.

Here are some of the ways in which a coin can be hidden in your hand. First, try them out to see which you find the easiest. Then practise your favourite technique until you are perfect before using it in a trick.

1 *The classic palming position, with the coin gripped between the base of your thumb and the edge of your hand. Try not to hold your fingers too stiffly or you will give the game away.*

2 *If you want to keep your fingers straight, you can hold the coin between two fingers, or between your thumb and the side of your hand.*

3 *This is the most difficult position, but it is the only way in which you can palm a coin if you have to show the audience the palm of your hand. The coin is held between two fingers at the back of your hand.*

THE VANISHING COIN

You will need: small coin ● glass tumbler ● large handkerchief or small scarf ● helper

In this trick you apparently put a coin in a glass tumbler and make it disappear!

First of all, say: 'Here, in this glass on my hand, is a penny (or whichever coin you decide to use). I am going to cover the glass with this scarf, and hand it to my friend, who has agreed to help me.'

Then pass the glass, with the scarf still covering it, to your helper, saying: 'Now, will you please remove the scarf.'

You helper does so, and, Abracadabra, the coin has vanished!

THE REAPPEARING COIN

✩ ✩ ✩ ✩ ✩

You will need: small coin ● member of the audience

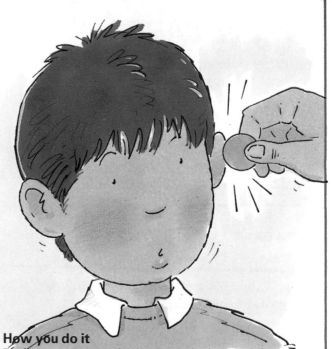

This is a very impressive trick, in which you make a coin appear out of a member of the audience's left ear! You have to be very good at palming to carry it out, so practise until you are perfect!

First, say to the audience: 'Remember the coin that disappeared from inside the glass? I am now going to make it reappear. May I have the help of a member of the audience, please?'

When someone steps forward, thank them, and say: 'Now, sir (or madam), I hope you washed your ears today, because I am going to tap you on the nose and show you where the coin has been hiding all this time – in your left ear!'

Then tap the member of the audience on the nose with one hand, and magically produce the coin with the other. Your helper, and the audience, will be astounded.

How you do it
Before you start, hide the coin in your hand using one of the palming methods described on the opposite page. (Use whichever hand you find easier.) Tap the member of the audience on the nose with the other hand, move the hand with the coin in it to behind his or her ear, then produce the coin with a flourish. You could also produce it from behind a person's neck, elbow, or knee.

How you do it
Put the coin on the palm of your hand *underneath* the glass – it is never inside it. Then cover the glass completely with the scarf or handkerchief, and as you lift it in one hand to give it to your helper, conceal the coin in the palm of the other hand. Then, while your helper is removing the scarf and all eyes are on the glass, slip your hand into a pocket, let go of the coin, and quickly take your hand out again before anyone has time to become suspicious. It is easiest to use a small coin if your hands are not very big. As with all tricks, the more you practise, the easier it will be to perform. You will baffle your audience more easily too!

ON THE CARDS

Card tricks are among the most popular – and the most baffling – that a magician performs. Playing cards were first used in the East, and came to Europe as long ago as the fourteenth century. However, it was not until 200 years later that the pack of fifty-two cards with four 'suits' became popular. The 'suits' are hearts and diamonds (red) and spades and clubs (black), and each contains thirteen cards. Number one is called the ace, and is usually classed as the highest card, although it has the lowest number. The other numbered cards go up to ten, but each pack also contains 'court' cards. These are the jack or knave, the queen and the king. The king is the highest card below the ace.

PICK A CARD

You will need: pack of cards • box with a lid, such as a shoebox • paperclip

Say to the audience: 'I have here an ordinary pack of cards. Perhaps you would like to examine it.' Hand the complete pack over to the audience so that they can see there is nothing wrong with it.

Then say: 'Now, would each of you please choose a card? Remember what it is, but don't tell me, and don't show me. Hold out the cards face downwards so I can't see them, and give them back to me. I'm going to put them in this box with the rest of the pack, put the lid on, and shake them about.' Then put the selected cards into a shoebox with the other cards from the pack.

Now say: 'Right. Now (speaking to the person who took the first card) can you tell me what your card was, madam? The two of spades? (You then rummage around in the box, without looking in it, and produce a card. Hold it out to show the audience – it is the two of spades.) Here it is.'

How you do it
The secret of this trick lies in organization – and a paperclip, which is hidden in the shoebox. As you take the chosen cards back from the audience and put them into the box, slip the paperclip on them to keep them in order. Keep them carefully in the same order, and face down, so that the first card collected will be the bottom card facing downwards. Put the paperclip on so its longer side is resting on the first card (you will easily be able to feel which side of the paperclip is which), and then you will know which card to take out first. You also have to remember to ask the people what their cards were in the order in which you gave them out, and collect them back in the same order, or the trick will not work.

If you concentrate hard and do the trick properly, it will make a tremendous impression on the audience.

THE KING IN EXILE

You will need: two identical packs of cards •
some glue • scissors

In this trick the King of Hearts disappears
and then reappears in your pocket!

First, show your audience four or five
cards, arranged as shown in the illustration
below, with the King of Hearts in the centre.
Then say: 'The King of Hearts is really rather
a lazy king. He doesn't much like ruling his
kingdom, and prefers pottering in his garden
and growing roses. So, when his courtiers
come to ask him to make important
decisions, they can never find him.'

As you are saying this you close the cards
up again, and when you get to the end of your
speech you reopen them – and the king has
vanished!

Then continue your story. 'The people got
so cross with their king that they forced him
to live in exile. And that is where he is now.'
As you say this, reach into your pocket – and
pull out the King of Hearts!

How you do it
Make a trick card by taking the King of
Hearts from one pack, cutting it in half, and
gluing one of the halves over another card.
Hide the complete King of Hearts from
another pack in your pocket.

When you start the story, hold the cards as
shown in the illustration. As you talk, close
up the cards, then pass them into your other
hand so they are the other way up. When you
talk about the courtiers not being able to find
their king, open the cards the other way up –
and the king has gone! In fact the other side
of the card is on show instead. Finally, at the
end of your story, pull the ordinary King of
Hearts card from your pocket.

Now you see it, now you don't

THE DISAPPEARING PENCIL

You will need: pencil • large handkerchief you cannot see through • loose-sleeved jacket

In this trick you hold a pencil up in full view of the audience, cover it with a handkerchief, whisk the handkerchief away – and discover the pencil has vanished!

First say: 'Here is a perfectly ordinary pencil. I am going to cover it with this handkerchief.' Then count to three and remove the handkerchief. Abracadabra! The pencil has vanished!

How you do it
First of all you must be wearing a jacket with full-length loose sleeves. Assuming you are right-handed, hold the pencil in your right hand and put the handkerchief over it with your left hand. As you do so, hold up the first finger of your right hand, so that it takes the place of the pencil under the handkerchief. Let the pencil drop down your sleeve. The audience will not be able to tell you are doing this if you practise the trick until you can do it with ease. Wait a few moments to make the trick seem more impressive, then whisk the handkerchief away with your left hand, remembering not to leave your finger sticking up. Keep your right hand upright, and open it to show your audience that it is empty. Then, while chatting to the audience and waving the handkerchief around with your left hand, slip your right hand into your pocket and let the pencil slide down your sleeve into it.

HERE TODAY, GONE TOMORROW

You will need: small coin • glass tumbler • pencil • two sheets of white paper • scissors • glue • some coloured paper, or a sheet of newspaper

In this trick you cover a coin with a glass, cover the glass with some coloured paper or newspaper rolled into a cone shape, and make the coin disappear and then reappear.

First say: 'Here, on this sheet of white paper is a small coin, and here is a glass. I am going to cover the glass with this cone and put the glass over the coin. If I say the magic word "abracadabra", and lift off the cone – the coin has disappeared! And now I'm going to put back the cone and wave my magic wand over it. Now if I lift up the cone and the glass, we will find that the coin has returned!'

How you do it
This trick is much easier to do than it looks. The secret lies in the preparation. First of all, make a circle of white paper exactly the size of the top of the glass. Do this by standing the glass upside down on the paper and drawing round it with a pencil. Cut out the circle and spread a thin layer of glue round the rim of the glass. The paper circle should then stick to it quite easily.

When the cone-covered glass (you need the cone so that the audience cannot see the

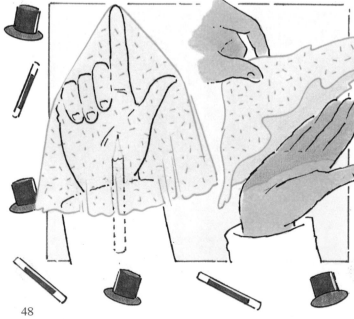

paper on the glass) is placed over the coin, the paper disc hides the coin, but when the glass and cone are removed, the coin is revealed. But don't make the mistake of lifting off the cone and not moving the glass, or your audience will soon realize how the trick works.

THE COIN THAT IS CHOPPED UP AND VANISHES

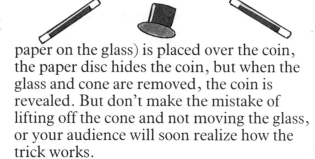

You will need: coin • piece of paper • scissors

In this trick you appear to chop a coin wrapped in a sheet of paper into pieces, to prove that it has vanished!

First say: 'I'm going to wrap up this coin in a piece of paper to make a little packet. Would you like to feel that it is still there (offering the packet to a member of the audience)? Right. Now I'm going to cut the packet, and the coin, into little pieces. And, lo and behold, the coin has vanished!' As you say this, scatter the cut-up bits of paper onto the table with a flourish.

How you do it
The secret of this trick lies in the way you wrap up the coin. Put it in the centre of the piece of paper and fold the paper into three

by folding the left and right sides over the middle. Then fold it in three horizontally, with the upper part of the paper folding down over the coin first. As this fold is made, slide the coin to the open end of the paper nearest you, then fold that third over the other two. The coin will now be in the open end, but when a member of the audience feels it, he or she will assume it is in the centre. You must be careful not to let it slip out too soon.

Once a member of the audience has felt the coin, let it slide into your hand and palm it. Hold the packet in your left hand, and as you slide your right hand across to pick up the scissors, let the coin drop out of sight into the table drawer or *servante*. The paper can then be chopped up without any problem.

STRAWDINARY!

These tricks should be presented as challenges to members of the audience – you, who know the secret, can do them, but they will probably rack their brains forever before hitting on the answer.

ELEVEN STRAWS

You will need: 11 drinking straws

Spread six of the straws out on the table as shown in the illustration below.

Keep the other five in a pile on one side.

Say to the audience: 'Here are six straws. I challenge anyone to add the five straws in that pile to these six, and end up with nine!'

How you do it

FIFTEEN STRAWS

You will need: 15 drinking straws

Lay out the fifteen straws on the table as shown in the illustration below.

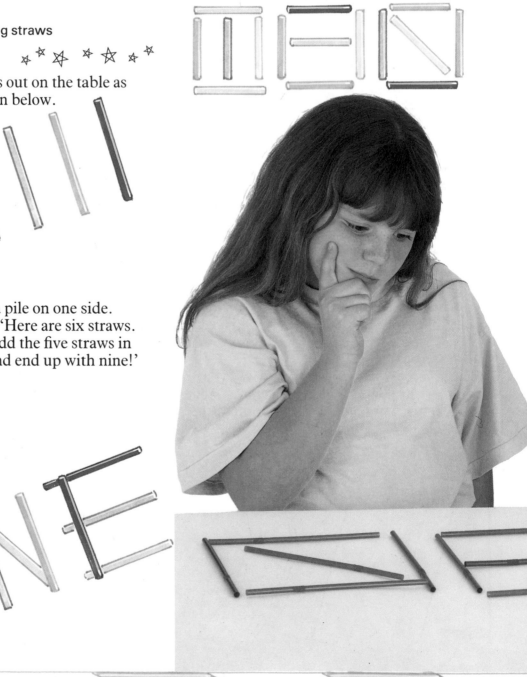

Then say to the audience: 'I challenge any of you to remove six straws from these fifteen, and leave ten behind!'

How you do it
Take away six straws and leave nine, forming the letters of the word TEN.

You will need: 8 drinking straws

This trick is really tantalizing, and guaranteed to drive your audience mad! Spread out the eight straws on the table, in no particular order or pattern. Then say: 'I challenge you to form three squares with these eight straws alone.'

The audience may think this is impossible, but they would be wrong.

How you do it

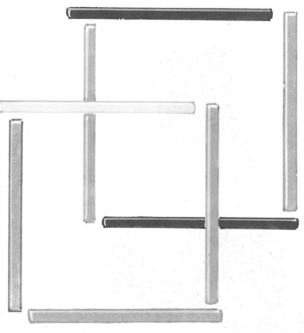

When you show your audience the solution, make sure that the middle shape is a true square and not a rectangle.

51

STRINGING ALONG

GONE FISHING

✦ ✶ ✦ ✦

You will need: glass or clear plastic bowl filled with water • ice cubes • pieces of string • salt

✦ ✦ ✦ ✦ ✦

First float some ice cubes in the bowl, and challenge the audience to fish one out using a piece of string.

Say: 'I can lift one of these ice cubes out of the water with this string. Would one of you like to try it first? No, don't tie the string round the ice cube, sir. It will slip off. Shall I show you how to do it?'

Then you dip the end of the string in the water, and pick up an ice cube with it!

How you do it

Before you start, put a small pile of salt behind the bowl. While you are challenging your audience to pick up an ice cube, dip the end of your piece of string in the water, and then, before you demonstrate how to do it, dip the wet end of the string into the salt. Do not let the audience see you do it or you will give the game away. Then, when you dip your string into the water again to go fishing, lay the salty end of it along the top of the ice cube for a few moments. The salt will melt the surface of the ice cube, which will then quickly freeze over again, sticking the end of the string to the ice. As a result, you will be able to pick up the cube with ease.

CUT AND COME AGAIN

✦ ✶ ✦ ✦ ✦

You will need: piece of string • cardboard tube, such as the inside of a toilet roll or kitchen towel roll • scissors

✦ ✦ ✦ ✦ ✦

In this trick you thread the string through the cardboard tube, cut the tube in half, and produce the string magically restored to one piece again!

First say: 'Look at this tube, ladies and gentlemen. You can see that it is hollow, and that there is nothing hidden in it. I am now going to thread the string through the tube. You can see, if I pull it one way and then the other, that it really does pass through the tube. Now I am going to cut the tube in half – and, abracadabra, the string is magically restored to one piece!'

How you do it

Prepare the tube beforehand by cutting two small slits in the back of it. Then feed the string through the slits, outside the tube, and cut the tube *inside* the string, so that the string itself is not actually cut at all. You will

RING ON A STRING

✫ ✫ ✫ ✫ ✫ ✫

You will need: approximately 1 m of string ●
2 identical rings cut out of cardboard and big
enough for you to put your fist through ●
loose sleeved jacket

✫ ✫ ✫ ✫ ✫ ✫ ✫

First get a member of the audience to tie one
end of the string round one of your wrists and
the other end round the other wrist.
Encourage them to tie the string quite tightly
at both ends.

   Say: 'You can see that this string is tied
firmly round my wrists. Now, can one of you
pass me the ring. Thank you. Now I'll just
turn round, say the magic words, and – look,
the ring is threaded on the string! You might

have to do this very skilfully of course, so that
your audience doesn't notice. Improve your
presentation by continual practice until you
get it just right.

like to check that the string is still tied to my
wrists. (Let a member of the audience have a
good look.) It is? Well, this really is an
amazing magic ring, isn't it?'

How you do it
You have *two* magic rings. One you slip over
your wrist and hide up your sleeve before you
start. When you turn away from the
audience, you slip the ring the audience saw
into your pocket, and let the ring up your
sleeve slide down on to the string.

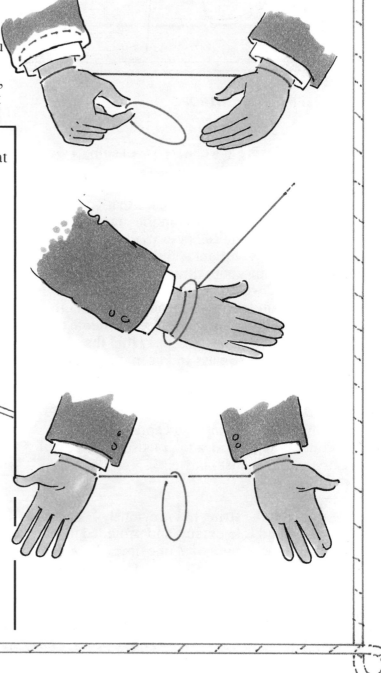

WATER PERFORMANCE!

DRY WATER

You will need: glass • water • pepper

Challenge your audience to dip a finger in a glass of water without getting it wet. Say: 'I know how to put my finger into this glass of water without getting it wet. Can any of you do it? I bet you can't!'

How you do it
Sprinkle a layer of pepper all over the surface of the water. Then, if you dip your finger in slowly and carefully, the pepper will prevent the water from touching you and your finger will remain dry.

WATER ON A TIGHTROPE

You will need: jug • glass • 1 m of string • water

First explain to your audience that you are going to make the water in the jug walk a tightrope, so you can pour it, over a distance, into the glass without spilling any.

Fill the jug about three-quarters full with water, and wet the string. Tie the string to the jug handle and pass it across the mouth of the jug to the spout, and then down into the glass, as shown on the right. Hold the end of the string in the glass and keep it taut. Now pour the water out of the jug, with the jug raised higher than the glass. If you pour gently, the water will 'walk' along the string to the glass and you won't spill a drop. It would be a good idea to practise over the sink first, though, just in case!

How you do it
As long as the string has previously been wetted, and is kept taut, and provided not too much water is poured at one time, the water will travel along the string and will not spill. (However, even when you are very skilled at this trick, it is advisable to keep a cloth to hand to mop up any water that gets away!)

SWIM, SWIM LITTLE FISH

You will need: bowl of water (or the sink or bath) • 'fish' cut out of paper (see illustration) • teaspoon • cooking oil

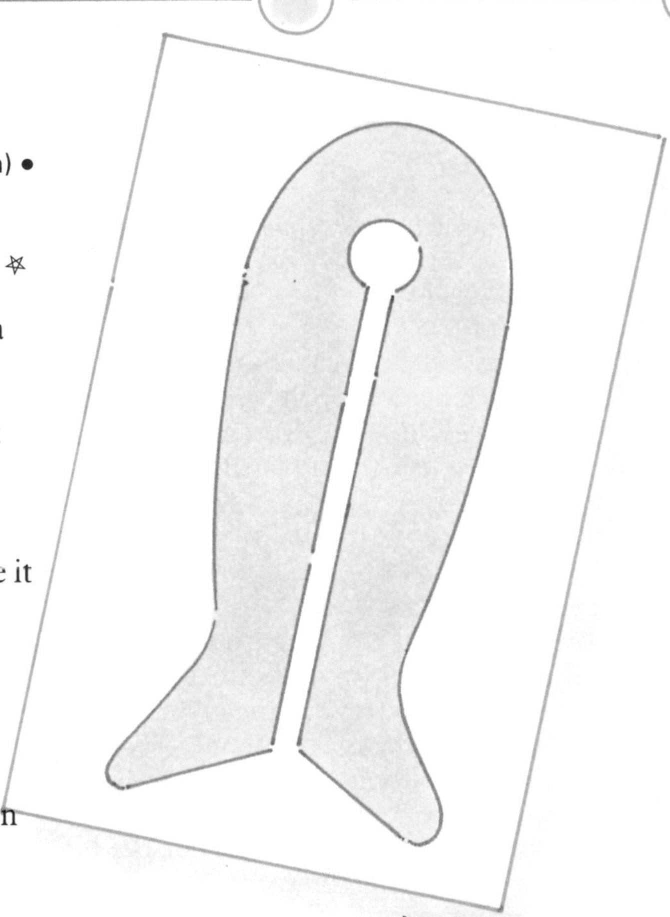

Cut out the fish as shown on the right, with a hole in its centre and a narrow channel leading from the hole to its tail. Say: 'I can make this fish swim across this bowl without either blowing it or touching it. Can any of you do that?'

It is unlikely that any member of the audience will be able to, but you can achieve it quite easily!

How you do it

Start with the fish at one end of the bowl. Pour a little oil into the teaspoon, and from there into the hole in the centre of the fish. The oil will spread into the channel and down to the fish's tail, so propelling the fish forward.

PAPER POWER

CLIMBING THROUGH A POSTCARD

You will need: postcard or piece of paper the same size • scissors

Say to your audience: 'I can climb through this postcard. You don't believe me, do you? Would any of you like to have a go first?'

The audience will be mystified, but you take up the scissors, make a few quick cuts, and climb through the postcard!

How you do it

Fold the postcard in half lengthways and make alternate cuts from opposite sides into it as shown below, never cutting all the way across. Cram in as many cuts about $\frac{1}{2}$ cm apart as you can without tearing the card. When you have done that, open out the fold and cut along it between the points marked in the illustration, leaving the two ends uncut. Open the card out, and you will find you can easily climb through the ring it makes.

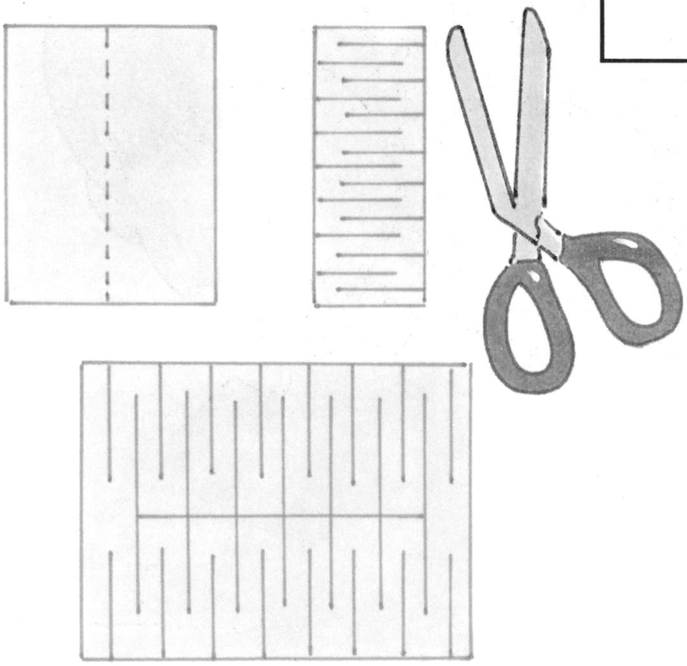

THE MAGIC RING

You will need: A4 size piece of paper • pen or pencil • sticky tape or glue • scissors • helper

Cut a strip off the long side of the piece of paper and make a magic ring out of it – a ring that has only one side and which cannot be cut into two!

Say to the audience: 'I have here a special magic ring. Would you, sir, like to try cutting it in two? Here are the scissors – have a try.' And your helper will try, and be left with one, larger ring, instead of two!

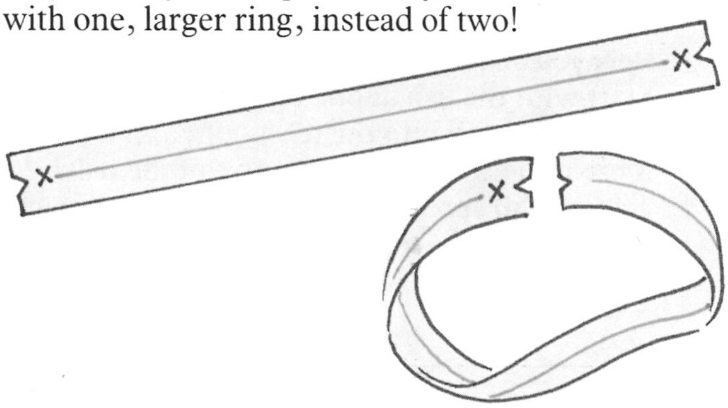

How you do it

Cut a strip off your paper about 2 cm wide. Mark each end with a cross on one side only and draw a line between the two crosses. Draw a similar line on the other side. Twist the strip of paper once, then stick the two ends together, so that the crosses meet. If you now try to trace the line round the paper, you will discover that the ring only appears to have one side, and if you cut along the line, you will not be left with two rings but with one double-sized one. If, however, you try to cut the new ring in half, you will be left with two interlocked rings!

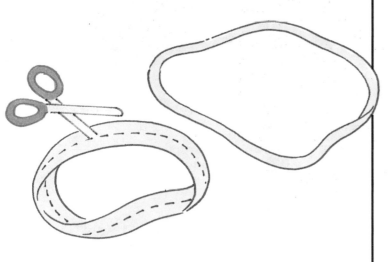

How you do it

Start with two identical sheets of newspaper (the front page is a good idea because it is easily recognizable). Fold one sheet into a tiny bundle, and glue it to the back of the other sheet as shown below. Then hold up the paper, with the bundle at the back facing you, and tear the sheet in half, then in half again, and so on, always keeping the folded sheet hidden and the torn pieces in front of it. When you roll the torn pieces into a ball, unfold the bundle and produce the magically restored paper, keeping the torn pieces hidden in your hand.

THAT'S TORN IT!

✷ ✷ ✷ ✷ ✷ ✷

You will need: 2 copies of the same newspaper ● glue

✷ ✷ ✷ ✷ ✷ ✷

In this trick you tear up a sheet of newspaper, crumple the pieces up into a ball, wave your magic wand over the ball, and magically produce the sheet of newspaper whole again!

First say: 'Here is the front page of *The Morning News* (give the real name of whichever paper you use). I'm going to tear it up into lots of little pieces, like this. Now, if I wave my wand over it and say a few magic words – the page is magically restored!'

CODES AND CIPHERS 1

Do you know the difference between a code and a cipher?

A keen spy will seize any opportunity to decipher his codes.

A code uses a word, a number, a letter, or a symbol to represent a word or group of words. A cipher has a different letter, number, or symbol for each letter in the alphabet. A code requires the use of a code book in which the code words and their meanings are given. This is a disadvantage because the book could fall into the wrong hands, but an advantage because, without the book, the code is indecipherable. A cipher does not require a 'key' as long as its users are aware of which cipher is being used. But its disadvantage is that it can often be cracked by those experienced in code-breaking.

CREATING A CODE

If you want to devise a secret code which no-one but the members of your group will understand, you need first to know roughly what kind of messages you are likely to want to transmit. For example, if you were a political spy, you would want to send messages about movements of ships and aircraft, of visits by politicians to foreign countries, and so on. If you were an industrial spy, you would be more concerned with methods of manufacture, materials, and movement of goods. Either way, you create a code word.

Suppose you were a spy for a company making television sets. You might want to send a message like this: *Latest Japanese model features remote-control video link*. And you might transcribe it like this: *Carrots teacup lawnmower flower apple*. *Carrots* means 'latest Japanese model', *teacup* means 'features', *lawnmower* means 'remote-control', *flower* means 'video' and *apple* means 'link'. Each person who will use the code keeps a code book in which the words and their meanings are listed and can be looked up to decipher messages and to send new ones.

MAKING A CIPHER WHEEL

Here's how to make a device which will give you lots of different options for creating ciphers. You will need some thin card, a pair of compasses, a pencil or pen, and a paper fastener.

1   Using the compasses, or by drawing round the rim of a cup and a saucer, make two circles of card, one about 10 centimetres (4 inches) in diameter and one about 7 centimetres (2¾ inches). Cut them out carefully.
2   Mark the circles as shown in the illustration. The larger disc is lettered and numbered in a clockwise direction; the smaller one is lettered anticlockwise.
3   Make a small hole in the centre of both discs and push a paper fastener through it to hold both discs together yet allow one to revolve upon the other.
4   The cipher wheel is now ready for use. Before you can use it, you need a key letter. Let us suppose it is S.
5   Turn the larger wheel so that its S is opposite the letter A on the smaller wheel. Then you can create the code by using the letters on the smaller wheel as the 'real' ones, and the letters or numbers on the larger wheel as the ciphers.

Here is an example. Using S as the key letter, the word 'contact' can be made into a cipher as Q E F Z S Q Z or as 17 5 6 26 19 17 26.

Make your own code wheel using a plan like this. The smaller wheel inside can be revolved in either direction.

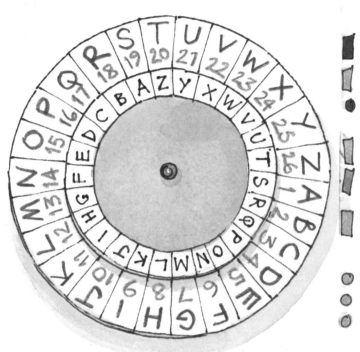

Each person involved in using the cipher will need to make his or her own wheel, and can then be sent any message provided the key letter is given, usually at the beginning of the message.

What does the message below say?
(D) WDIZ YJQ BMZDKVQX BPAZL

Answer: 'Have fun creating codes'

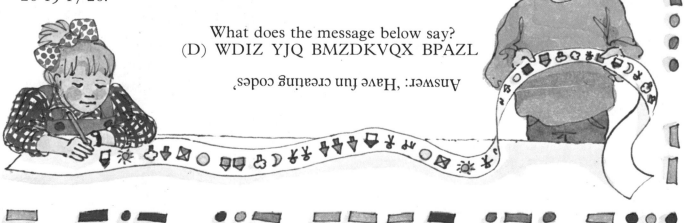

CREATING A DISGUISE

If you want to be a successful spy, able to carry out your activities without being recognized, you have to create a disguise. The best ways of doing this are by disguising your body and your face.

DISGUISING YOUR BODY

Clothing You may think it is impossible to make yourself into an entirely different shape but, with a little ingenuity, it can be done easily.

First of all, you need to borrow an old and preferably over-large coat, such as an old raincoat. You can then make yourself look fatter by strapping a cushion or a pillow round your middle, underneath the coat, and you can make yourself look taller by putting a rolled-up towel or sweater around the back of your neck and shoulders. If you are a girl, you can make yourself appear taller by wearing high-heeled shoes.

It is, of course, more difficult to make yourself look thinner or smaller, but a large, loose coat will hide your weight, and walking with a stoop will make you look shorter.

Movement Next, you have to learn to disguise your movements and mannerisms. If you are right-handed, try to do things with your left hand (and vice-versa), especially if you are being watched.

Then you must disguise your walk. If you normally walk quickly, cultivate a leisurely stroll; if you normally walk slowly, try to hurry a bit. Swing your arms as you go along, and carry an um-

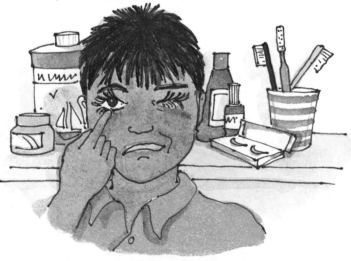

Right: Alec Guinness as John le Carré's spy, George Smiley.

Below left: Make sure you can walk in high-heeled shoes!

ACTING A PART

With a few 'props', you can act out a part which might make it easier for you to gain access to certain places. For example, if you have, or can borrow, a track suit, you can wear your plimsolls or training shoes, tie a band round your hair, and pretend to be a jogger. Carrying a bucket and a cloth, you could be cleaning cars, which gives you an opportunity to linger without being noticed. Wearing an old overall and carrying a broom you could be a road-sweeper, which also means that you can lurk and keep watch on someone. If you can get hold of a collection of really threadbare old clothes, tie a piece of string round your middle and settle down for a snooze in a doorway with your hat pulled over your eyes like an old tramp. But, of course, you won't really be asleep, you'll be keeping a careful ear and eye on everything that goes on.

brella, or a newspaper, or a briefcase, especially if you don't usually do so. Why not adopt a special limp or a stiff leg? So you do it properly, and don't forget which leg to limp with, or which one is stiff, put a pebble in one shoe to make you limp (you'll have to, it will hurt!) and tie a ruler (not too tightly) to the back of your knee with a scarf, handkerchief, or bandage so you can't bend it.

Opposite sex   If you want to appear to be of the opposite sex, then fasten your coat the other way round and, if the fasteners won't work that way, wrap the coat round and hold it with a belt. Try to walk with shorter steps if you want to appear to be a girl, and with longer ones if you want to appear to be a boy.

Disguised as a newspaper reporter or a market researcher you can use a tape recorder without arousing suspicion.

DISGUISING YOUR FACE

A face mask will hide your identity, but it may draw attention to you! Use a magazine for cutting out faces to fit you.

Two very good 'props' for making your face look completely different are a hat and a pair of dark glasses. If you tuck all your hair under a hat and pull it well down, you will look completely different. You can change your appearance further by folding the brim back, or wearing the hat on one side. A pair of dark glasses is a wonderful disguise, as every film star knows. If you want to look sinister, buy a pair with reflecting lenses so people cannot see your eyes.

Hair Your facial appearance can be changed a lot by changing your hair style. Part your hair in a different place; comb a fringe back or to one side; or, if you don't normally have a fringe then brush your hair forward to create one. If your hair is difficult to persuade to stay in a different style, then wet it first, or borrow some hair spray to hold it in place.

You can make yourself look older by rubbing talcum powder into your hair around the temples – then you'll look as if you're going grey.

If you are a girl and have longish hair, there are lots of ways of changing your appearance. You can hide it all under a hat or scarf; put it up in a bun; plait it; or create lots of different styles using clips and slides.

If you can borrow a wig or hairpiece, that would be splendid but, even if you can't, you might be able to buy some cheap crêpe hair from a joke shop. With it, you can have fun creating bushy eyebrows, beards, moustaches, or long hair sticking out from under your hat.

Make sure you are wearing the right disguise at the right time!

If you are trying to look like a man, rub some of the pencil or shadow around your chin, cheeks, and upper lip to create an unshaven appearance.

If you are trying to look like a glamorous and sophisticated woman, and you have access to make-up, you can try all of it, putting eye shadow on your eyelids, mascara on your eye lashes, powder on your face, blusher on your cheeks, and vivid lipstick on your lips, but take care. It takes a bit of practice to put on make-up properly and, if you go out with your lipstick all smudged and your eye make-up running, you will attract unnecessary attention, and spoil your carefully prepared disguise.

Make-up Theatrical make-up is ideal to create a really effective disguise, but there are other things you can resort to. You can make your skin look suntanned by rubbing a little cocoa powder on it, or you can make yourself look pale by rubbing talcum powder on your face.

If you can borrow some real make-up (do ask permission first), you can have a great time. An eye pencil or some eye shadow in grey or brown can be used to make you look older. Frown in front of a mirror and, where the creases appear across your forehead and at the sides of your mouth, draw in lines with the pencil or shadow. You will look years older!

INVISIBLE MESSAGES

When you have to pass a message to a contact you may well write it in a code or cipher, but to make it extra-specially secret, you should write it in invisible ink. Then it can only be read by the person for whom it was intended because anyone coming across it accidentally will never know it is there.

HOW TO MAKE INVISIBLE INK

Substances which can be used as invisible ink are found in every home. Almost any sugar solution – this means sugar dissolved in water – works well. About a teaspoonful of sugar in a glass of water is what you need. You can also try dissolving a teaspoonful of clear honey in a glass of warm water. Ordinary canned or bottled fizzy drinks work, too, because they contain sugar.

Fruit juices also make good invisible ink. The best kinds to use are orange, lemon, and grapefruit juices, which can either be squeezed out of the fruits or used from a bottle or carton. Apple juice works, too, but not quite as well as the others.

Milk makes good ink, too. It is best if it is not too creamy, or you may get greasy marks on the paper, which will give the game away. Neat vinegar works, and a teaspoonful of salt dissolved in a glass of water does too.

If you cannot find any of these things, cut a potato or an onion in half and scrape your 'pen' along the vegetable's surface to collect the juice.

HOW TO WRITE INVISIBLE MESSAGES

Before you can write a message, you need a 'pen'. You cannot use a real pen or pencil, or you will mark the paper, but

Concealing the tools of your trade is essential for a good spy. Containers and equipment for writing messages should be with you.

you could use the pointed cap of a ball-point pen, a matchstick, a toothpick, or even a small, clean twig. Pour your 'ink' into a small glass or an eggcup, dip your 'pen' into it, and write your secret message. Remember that you will not be able to see the message, so work out what you are going to say before you write. If necessary, write it down with a pencil first, then destroy the paper it was written on.

As an extra precaution, send your message on the back of a perfectly ordinary letter, or even on a birthday card. This is to prevent suspicion if it is intercepted. A piece of blank paper looks very suspicious!

You can also write a message with a piece of candle, although this has the disadvantage that it can be felt if you rub a finger over the paper.

HOW TO READ INVISIBLE MESSAGES

If the message is written with a candle, it can be made to appear by dusting the paper lightly with talcum powder or flour. The powder will stick to the message but not to the paper. Or you can rub a waxed crayon over it, or paint over the paper with water colour. The crayon or paint will stick to the paper but not to the wax and so the message will be revealed.

If you have written the message in invisible ink, then it can be made to appear by warming the paper. You must do this very carefully so that you don't set fire to it, for this would destroy the message as well as burning you! So warm it by holding it near a lighted bulb in a lamp, or near a central-heating radiator. *Never* hold the paper near a naked flame, a gas or electric cooker, a gas fire, or a radiant electric fire.

Once the paper has been warmed, the message will appear as light-brown writing. It cannot be made to vanish again so, when you have read the message, you will have to destroy the paper.

CODES AND CIPHERS 2

A /M	S /MM	A o▭	S ooo
B /MMM	T /\	B ▭ooo	T ▭
C /M/M	U /M/\	C ▭o▭o	U oo▭
D /M/	V /MM/	D ▭oo	V ooo▭
E /\	W /M/	E o	W o▭▭
F /MM/	X /M/M	F oo▭o	X ▭oo▭
G /M/	Y /M/M	G ▭▭o	Y ▭o▭▭
H /MMM	Z /M/M	H oooo	Z ▭▭oo
I /M	1 /MMM	I oo	1 o▭▭▭▭
J /MMM	2 /MMM	J o▭▭▭	2 oo▭▭▭
K /M/	3 /MMM	K ▭o▭	3 ooo▭▭
L /MMM	4 /MMM	L o▭oo	4 oooo▭
M /M	5 /MMM	M ▭▭	5 ooooo
N /M	6 /MMM	N ▭o	6 ▭oooo
O /M/	7 /M/M	O ▭▭▭	7 ▭▭ooo
P /M/M	8 /MMM	P o▭▭o	8 ▭▭▭oo
Q /M/M	9 /MMM	Q ▭▭o▭	9 ▭▭▭▭o
R /M/	10 /MMM	R o▭o	10 ▭▭▭▭▭

Can you work out what
the message above says?

Answer: 'All good spies know Morse'.

When Morse is
tapped out on
pipes, remember it
may well be heard
by someone other
than your contact!

MORSE CODE

Morse code is perhaps the best-known
code in the world. In fact, it is not a code
at all, but a cipher. It was created in the
nineteenth century by the American
inventor of the telegraph system, Samuel
Finley Breese Morse, and it uses a system
of dots and dashes to represent letters and
numbers. The picture above right shows
the standard form of Morse code; on the
left is an alternative way of representing it.

Morse can be transmitted in a number of ways. In the days of the telegraph, it was tapped out, using long and short taps. It is often flashed with a signalling lamp, and can even be played as music, by someone who is very clever.

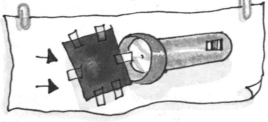

Taping a piece of red transparent plastic over a torch converts it into a daytime signalling device.

A Morse transmitting machine.

SEMAPHORE

Semaphore is a system which was devised for sending messages over quite long distances. It is the position of the signaller's arms which conveys the message but, because that could be difficult to see, flags are normally used. At the end of each word, a specific signal is given so the interceptor can read the message more easily.

What does this semaphore message say?

Answer: 'Keep codes in a safe place'.

DISGUISING YOUR VOICE

Learning how to disguise your voice is an important part of creating a really effective disguise, for it is no use looking completely different if your voice gives you away. Here are some ways of doing it. They all take a little practice and, if you have access to a tape or cassette recorder, and you can try out your new voice in private before using it in public, you will find it a great help.

ON THE TELEPHONE

It is easier to disguise your voice on the telephone than when you are face to face with someone because they cannot see what contortions you are making.

1 Put your tongue behind your lower front teeth when you speak. You will develop a lisp!

4 Try speaking with your thumb or a finger in your mouth.

2 Hold your nose between your thumb and first finger to make your voice sound as if you suffer from swollen adenoids. The tighter you hold it, the more pronounced will be the effect.

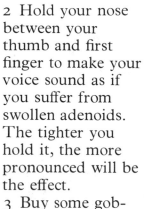

5 Spread a cotton handkerchief over the mouthpiece of the phone and speak through that.

3 Buy some gob-stoppers and try talking with one in your mouth. But take care that you don't choke!

6 Tie a large handkerchief or a scarf round your face to cover your nose and mouth so you look like a bandit, and speak through it.

In addition, when speaking on the telephone, you can try out some of the ploys listed.

IN PERSON

Before you try out a new voice, make sure you have decided exactly how you are going to disguise it. Once you have decided, do not change your disguise. Otherwise you will sound most peculiar!

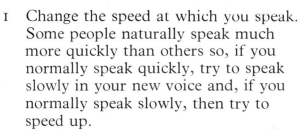

If you are being watched, you can try talking out of the side of your mouth.

1 Change the speed at which you speak. Some people naturally speak much more quickly than others so, if you normally speak quickly, try to speak slowly in your new voice and, if you normally speak slowly, then try to speed up.

2 Similarly, try to alter the pitch of your voice, that is, make it sound higher or lower than usual.

3 Cultivate an accent. This is difficult to do and requires lots of practice, but you can try to talk like someone from Scotland, Wales, Ireland, Australia, the southern United States or the Far East. If you want to be convincing, don't overdo it. A Scots accent with someone saying, 'Hoots, mon', all the time will just give you away!

MAKING YOUR ROOM SPY-PROOF

Once you become a spy, you have to be on the alert against enemy spies. They are probably just as anxious to listen to the conversations you have with your contacts, and to snoop around your room looking for code books and microfilm as you are to do the same to them!

You can also lay a false trail by leaving fake code books and messages around the place to put them off the scent – these are all ways of making your room spy proof. But there are other things you can do, too.

MAKING AN ALARM

If you are in another part of the house or garden and you want an instant warning of anyone entering your room, or if you are holding a meeting in your room and want warning of anyone approaching, you need to make an alarm. All you need are two or three empty drinks cans, a longish piece of string or fine black thread, and two or three large paperclips, used matchsticks, or hair grips.

To make an alarm which will warn you if someone enters your room, cut the string into as many pieces as you have tin cans. To one end of each piece of string attach the large paperclip, used matchstick, or hair grip, by knotting the string firmly around it. Carefully pin the other ends of the string together to the lintel on the outside of the door of your room. Then, by folding it flat back against the string, insert the paperclip, matchstick, or hair grip of each piece into the hole left by the ring-pull section of the can, and twist it round across the hole so that the can is suspended from the string. Then, as soon as someone opens the door, the cans will jangle together and instantly warn you of the interloper's presence.

If you want to position the alarm some distance from your room to warn you of someone approaching, you will need the same equipment as described above, but the string should be replaced by fine black cotton. Attach the cotton to the cans in the same way as before, and stretch the cotton, about 4 centimetres (1½ inches) off the ground, across the corridor or other place along which a spy would have to

OTHER SECURITY SYSTEMS

If you cannot manage to make an alarm and you want to know if someone has been in your room, there are other things you can do.

First of all, you can stick fine hairs or very thin pieces of thread across the doors of cupboards or across drawers in which you keep your papers and secret equipment. Then, if anyone opens the cupboards or drawers, they will break the hairs or threads, and you will be able to tell at a glance that they have been there.

Then, you can dust for fingerprints. Before you do this it is as well to know what your own fingerprints look like.

Take a clean, polished glass and hold it with all the fingers of your right hand. If your fingertips are not very greasy and do not easily leave prints you could borrow a little hand cream, or rub a little butter on them, before grasping the glass. When you have left a set of prints, wipe your hand clean and carefully brush a little flour or talcum powder over the glass. The prints will be clearly revealed. To file them for future reference, carefully stretch a piece of transparent adhesive tape across them, and then, equally carefully, stick it on a piece of dark-coloured paper or card. Repeat the procedure for your left hand.

Follow the same sequence when you are dusting equipment in your room for the fingerprints of intruders. These, too, can be fixed with powder or flour and stuck on to a card so you can compare them with your own. Once you are sure they are not yours, or those of your contacts, you may be able to find out to whom they belong.

walk to approach your room. Pin one end of the thread to the wall or skirting board, and tuck the cans away in a pile out of sight at the other end of the thread, with it stretched taut. If someone approaches, he or she will trip over the thread and pull down the pile of cans, making a terrible noise and warning you that the person is there.

FIRST YOU START WITH A BODY

Whatever you do, do not try to draw your cartoon starting at the head and working down. It is a good idea to think of drawing it in the same way as if you were getting dressed. You would not put on your shoes first and then try to get your socks on. You put on your clothes in the correct order until you are fully dressed. It is the same with drawing a cartoon. There is no short cut to doing it. You start with the basic construction and then build on it until you have a complete drawing.

This section describes how you build that first, basic construction. You should make these drawings on thin layout paper.

● Heads are generally egg shaped, so draw an egg.

● Put in a neck.

● Draw a rectangle for the body.

For the arms, draw in two sausage shapes with flat ends, the lower ends reaching to where the top of the legs will be.

Draw in two more sausages with flat ends, and make them a bit longer than the arms. These are the legs.

Draw two mittens, thumbs inwards, on to the ends of the arms. You have drawn the hands.

Similarly, for feet, draw two flat ovals on to the ends of the legs.

Now we can start to make the body look better. At the moment, the shoulders look as though there is a coat hanger in them, so slope them down a little. Make a waist, too, about half way down the rectangle. Look at your own arms. They go in a little at the elbows, and in again at the wrists. The legs, too, should go in a little at the knees and ankles. Make the

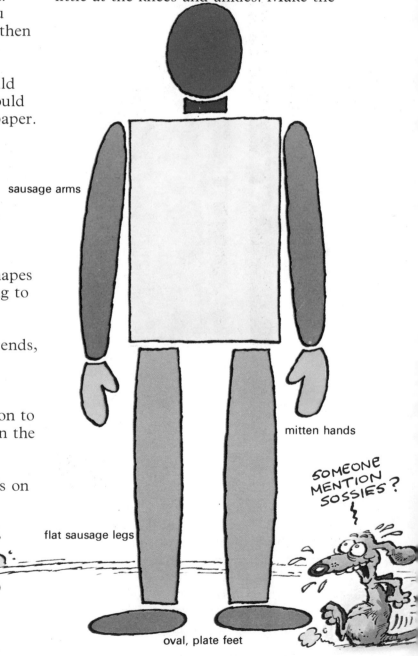

sausage arms

mitten hands

flat sausage legs

oval, plate feet

SOMEONE MENTION SOSSIES?

legs meet at the top where they join the rectangle.

Now you are thinking that you have never seen a real person who looks like your drawing. This is where you use your light box. Take this first drawing that you have just made, lay it flat on the glass, and put another sheet of paper on top. With the light switched on you should be able to see your first drawing clearly through the top sheet.

If you want to have another go at it, take another sheet of paper and trace a better figure through on to your new sheet. If you are still not happy, simply try again, and again, as many times as you want.

LIGHTBOX

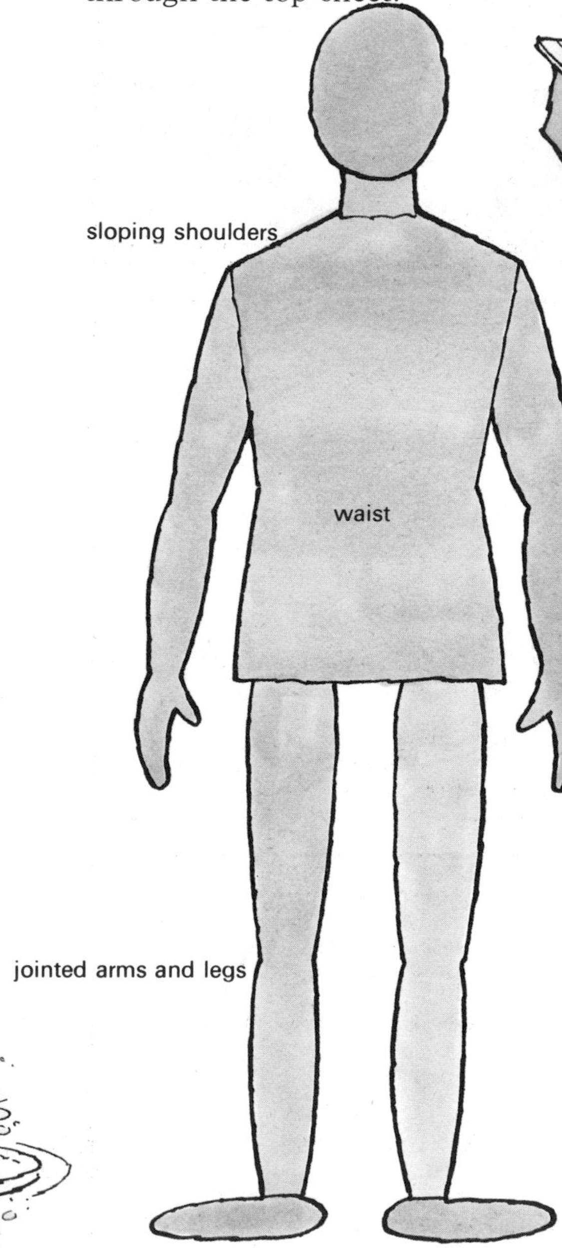

sloping shoulders

waist

jointed arms and legs

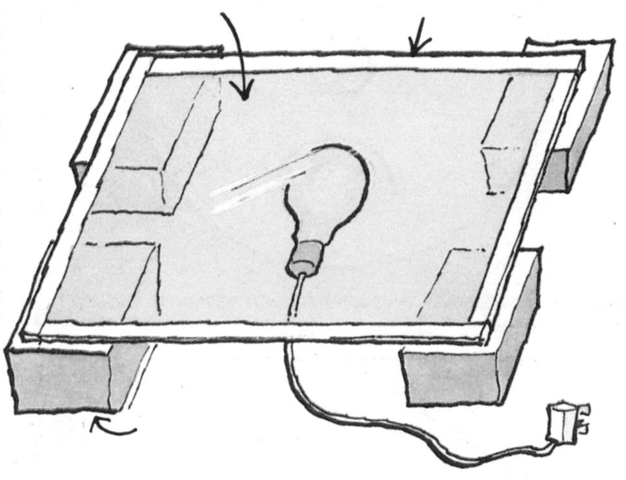

Light box A professional one is expensive, but an adequate substitute can be made quite easily with your parents' help. It is made from a small sheet of glass, a few books, and a light bulb. There is a picture of how it works and you will see how it can be used later. But leave this to an adult. Do not fiddle with glass or with electricity.

73

LET'S FACE IT

Now you have a good idea of how to build up the framework of the body, it's time to go further. Let's start with the face.

All you need is a series of circles, one circle for the nose and two for the eyes. Put in a line for the mouth. Now you have to decide what kind of person you want this figure to be.

Why not decide to draw a big, fat, happy man? So, draw a big smile where you had a straight line before. He really looks happy.

Here's an example of a smiling face going through a series of mood changes: sad; angry; surprised; laughing.

no expression

an upturned mouth gives a very different appearance

downturned eyebrows and mouth indicate sadness

what an angry face! note the frown and the shadows

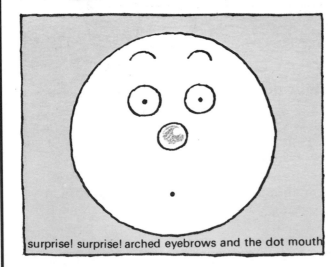

surprise! surprise! arched eyebrows and the dot mouth

laughter lines – upturned mouth, and half-moon eyes

BLEEP!
DOINK!

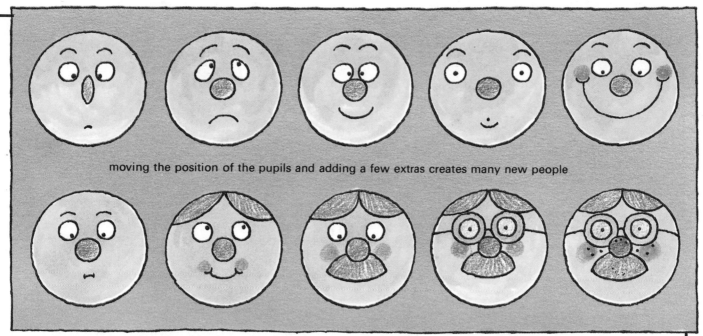

moving the position of the pupils and adding a few extras creates many new people

Once you have drawn your basic construction, you can do whatever you like with it. Change the shape of the nose. Then change the eyes. Try moving the eyes closer together and then further apart. Try the mouth. Make it very wide. Now make it very small. Try different hairstyles. Put moustaches on some of your men. Add a pair of spectacles. What about some freckles? And, don't forget to move the eyeballs around.

Now try changing the shape of the head. You can still begin with a circle but, once you have done that, make it wider at the top and narrower at the bottom. Then try it the other way round. You can spend hours inventing different-looking people.

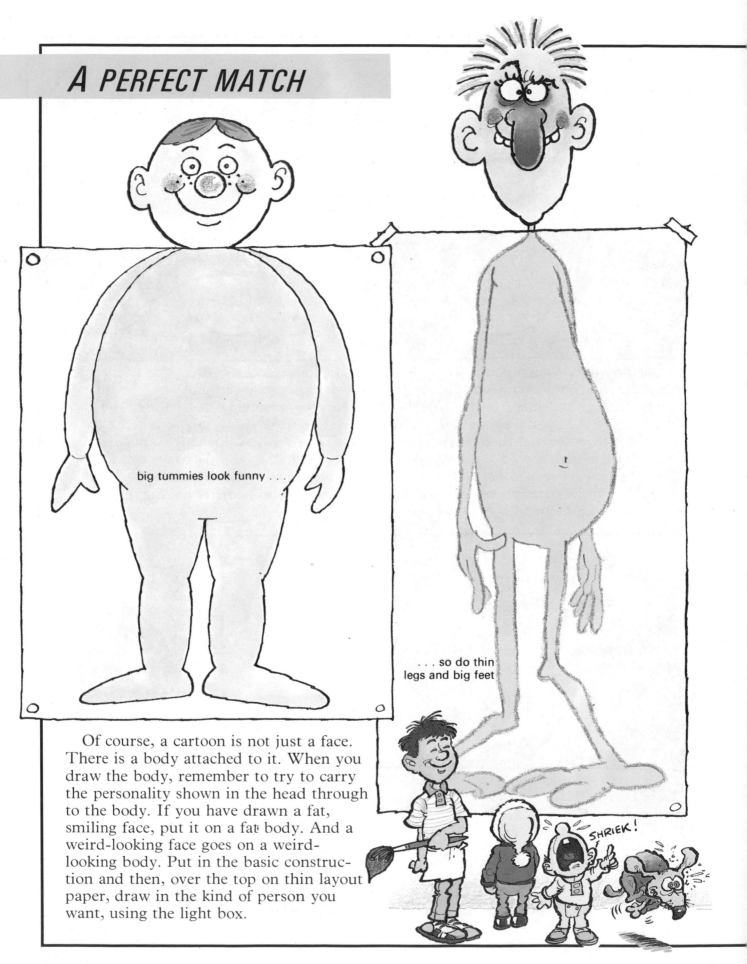

A PERFECT MATCH

big tummies look funny . . .

. . . so do thin legs and big feet

Of course, a cartoon is not just a face. There is a body attached to it. When you draw the body, remember to try to carry the personality shown in the head through to the body. If you have drawn a fat, smiling face, put it on a fat body. And a weird-looking face goes on a weird-looking body. Put in the basic construction and then, over the top on thin layout paper, draw in the kind of person you want, using the light box.

SHRIEK!

the bare bones

adding simple clothes brings your body to life

When you have decided on your body, put on the kind of clothes you think will suit the person. If you have drawn a young person, dress him or her in appropriate clothes such as sweatshirt, jeans, and trainers. Older people could look very silly in jeans and sweatshirts, so you might dress them more formally. On the other hand, you might want to make them look silly on purpose!

Don't forget hands and feet. You can make them both very big, indeed, and hands and feet can be very expressive.

ZOOMING ALONG!

So far, you have drawn your figures so that you are looking at their fronts. And they have been stationary.

Now you have to make the drawing turn. This will mean that an arm or a leg will be partly hidden behind the body.

When you do the basic construction, always draw in the whole arm or leg. Then, when you come to trace over the construction, just leave out the bits that you won't see.

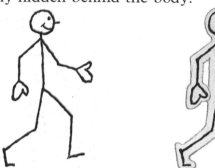

It is quite easy to make a figure move. Start by drawing a stick figure walking along. Think about the way you walk. Notice that your left leg moves forward together with your right arm. So draw the stick figure in that position. Using this figure as your 'model', draw a cartoon figure in a similar pose. Now try to make the stick figure run and, using it as your model again, draw the cartoon.

In general, to make their point, cartoonists draw very extreme action. For example, if the figure is running, it should be really zooming along. So you should emphasize the action.

Here is what you would normally do if you were running along.

But here's what a cartoonist would draw if he or she was told to draw the same action.

exaggerate the body's angle

feet right off the ground

puffs of smoke suggest speed

Experiment with your stick people. Make them do all kinds of different types of actions, and then construct your cartoons around them.

THROB

How to draw animals

The method for drawing animals is exactly the same as the one used for drawing the human figure. Taking into account the obvious differences in the various animals that we all know, you can use this method to draw almost any animal.

As with the human figure, start with the body.

Then add the head, neck, and legs.

If the animal has a tail or a trunk, now is the time to put them in.

make sure your paper is the right shape

You can use the methods we have already talked about to change their expression; after all, most animals do have two eyes, a nose, and a mouth.

GULP!

Do not be put off by being faced with having to draw an animal. As with the people you've already drawn, once you have the basic shape of your creature, you can then help yourself by looking in a book at a photograph of the creature you are drawing.

bulging eyes and nostrils look very comical

BLEEP! DOINK!

You can even make up some weird-looking animals of your own.

STRIP CARTOONS

At first glance, it looks very easy to draw a strip cartoon. A published comic strip takes about four professional people to put it together, however; the editor, a writer, an artist, and a lettering artist. You will have to be quite well organized if you are going to produce your own strip.

First, you must write the 'script'. Try to think of the character first and then write the story. A long story should contain about twelve to fourteen frames, a short one three or four. Leave one frame at the beginning for the title.

Now you have to draw up the 'grid'.

Here is a sample of one page that will take about twelve frames.

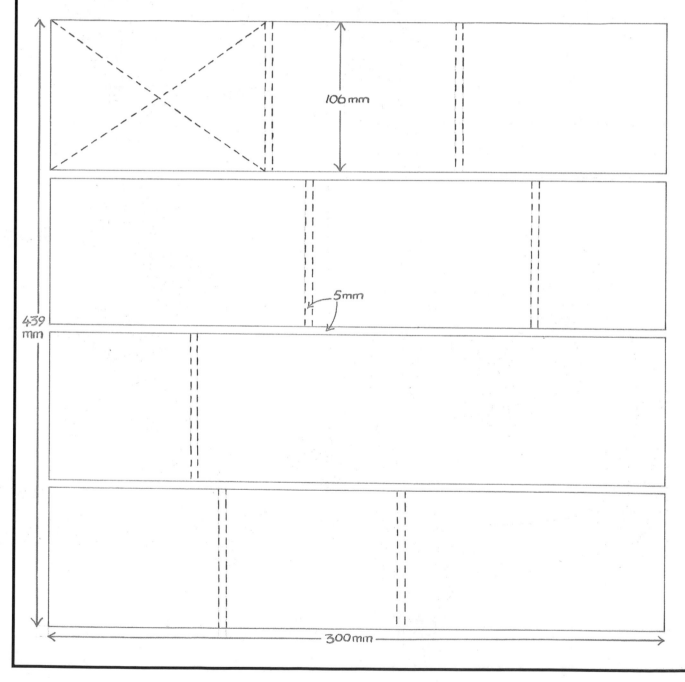

Strip cartoons are drawn much larger than they will appear in print. This is to make it easier for the cartoonist to draw it. Let's look at the script to see how many frames you have written. In this case, you find that you have written eleven frames. Look at the grid and you

When you start drawing, you must allow for the speech balloons to be drawn in. Always position the drawing in the bottom two-thirds of the frame. The action should move from left to right – the way you read. Make the action very clear and simple, so that the point of your

will see that there are four rows of pictures. That will give you three rows of three pictures and one row of two. This tells you that you should try to place the pictures in the text with the most action, on that row. So the pictures will be much bigger. The pictures with hardly any action will be very small.

story is easily understandable at the first glance.

When you have finished pencilling it in, put the caption lettering into the balloons and make the speech mark from the balloon come directly from the mouth of the person who is speaking. Now you can ink it in.

HASN'T AUNTY VERA GOT A BIG NOSE?

Drawing caricatures is another branch of cartooning. The secret of drawing a caricature of someone is to try to decide what is the most prominent feature of that person. Whenever you hear of someone being talked about, try to imagine him or her in your mind. For example, Uncle Fred is very fat or Aunty Vera has a big nose. It is this that makes the caricature. Concentrate on that main feature. Then draw your cartoon, and make that feature very prominent indeed. You can distort the face as much as you like. In fact, the more you do, the better it will be.

BE PREPARED

If you're just going out into the garden, to a park, or just for a gentle ramble locally, you hardly need to prepare for much, other than wondering whether or not it's going to rain and what time you're expected back for dinner! On the other hand, the countryside can be demanding, so you ought to decide what sort of "out and about" you have in mind. Read a few books and magazines, watch some T.V. programmes, or join a local rambling, jogging, or orienteering club – you'll soon discover what particularly attracts you about being out and about.

You may have a dream that one day you'll be a famous mountaineer, tackling the north-west face of Everest in winter, or you might be content just to sit beside a local gravel pit identifying the birds on the water. But whatever the case, it's wiser (and more fun in the end) to be prepared.

Always make sure that someone knows where you're going and, if you're venturing into wild country, even if it's only for a few hours, you should never be alone. It's best always to be accompanied by a responsible adult who is experienced in the ways of the wild.

KEEPING FIT

Country walking is not only good fun – it's good for you! Regular exercise is essential if you're going to lead a healthy life, and is a really good back-up to almost every sport imaginable. But if you're planning to tackle any more demanding pursuit, such as rock climbing, fell walking, long-distance walking, or jogging, then it would be safer and more enjoyable if you were fit and properly warmed up *before* you go.

If you're lucky enough to have a gym or leisure centre nearby, then there'll quite likely be many other attractions which will also help you to get fit – from swimming to aerobics. On the other hand,

WARMING-UP EXERCISES

Knee bends
Stand with your feet a little apart. Bend your knees until you are almost in a squatting position. Then return to the standing position and repeat ten times.

Ankle hug
Standing on one leg, bend the other back from the knee, clutching your ankle behind your back with both hands. Gently pull with your hands until the muscles at the front of your thighs feel taut. Do not pull too hard. Relax and repeat with the other leg.

there are plenty of exercises that you can practise at home. Try some of these with a friend or, failing that, play some of your favourite music while you're working out. It all helps to keep you going! Basically, there are three kinds of exercises: warming up and stretching exercises; exercises to improve your muscle strength and endurance; and those to improve the performance of your heart and lungs.

Step-ups
This is a good one to do if you have a low sturdy bench to step up on to. Using alternate legs, step up on to the bench and then down again. Continue until you begin to feel a little breathless.

Sit-ups
Lie on the floor with your hands behind your head, and your feet held down (ask a friend to help you). Trying to keep your legs as straight as you can, sit up until your head almost touches your knees. Lie back again. Repeat ten times. This is a good way to tighten your tummy muscles.

Wall stretch
This is to stretch the calf muscles and Achilles tendons (the muscle above the heel at the ankle). Stand facing the wall with your arms outstretched so that the flat of your hands are on the wall. Bend your arms, keeping your feet flat on the floor, until you are leaning forward and you can feel the muscles being stretched.

Thigh shift
Extend one leg backwards and the other forwards with the knee bent. Try again, using the other leg stretched backwards.

Even dogs need to be fit to accompany their owners into the Welsh hills.

Knee hug
Standing on one leg, bring the other one up in front of you, bending it at the knee, and clutching your knee with both hands. Gently pull it towards you until you can feel the muscles tightening. Do not pull too hard. You can also do this lying on your back. This exercise stretches the hamstrings.

DRESSED FOR THE PART

Your everyday clothes (tracksuits, jeans, T-shirt, and trainers, for example) are fine for casual outdoor wear in good weather. But if you're planning to venture far away from home then the clothes, including your footwear, that you wear or carry with you are very important.

Once again, it's a case of being prepared. Different kinds of walking, in different kinds of country, have different needs. And, of course, there's always the chance that the weather will change, especially in places like the British hills. For example, if you're out walking in February, it's quite possible that during the middle of the day, it may become quite warm. On the other hand, a blazing hot day in July at the foot of Ben Nevis may turn into a snow storm at the top.

Whatever you wear should be comfortable and should fit you well. It needs to keep you warm and dry (without making you sweaty!) when it's cold and wet, and cool when it's hot. You should also be able to change what you're wear-ing to suit changing conditions. So the best idea is to wear several layers – you can always strip off bit by bit as and when necessary.

Trainers are ideal, unless you're walking somewhere that's likely to be very rough or wet. If trainers aren't suitable, there are three main types of footwear recommended, and these are described in detail below. Just try to remember that your boots or shoes have a lot of work to do. The soles should have a good grip to stop you skidding; they should protect the bottoms of your feet from any sharp stones and absorb the shock of perhaps thousands of footsteps. The uppers should be warm and waterproof for walking in cold, wet conditions, yet not too hot and sweaty; they should also help to protect the rest of your foot from damage and give support to the ankle if you're walking over uneven country. Above all, though, your boots or shoes should be as light as possible. It's hopeless trying to walk with great weights on the end of your legs!

These are called rock boots and are specially designed for rock climbers. The sole is made of a special sort of sticky rubber. These boots give a great grip on rocky walks.

These are rugged, heavy, leather mountain boots with a "Commando"-style rubber sole. They should be worn for very rough terrain and could be used in winter

when it's cold and wet The soles are very stiff – special spikes called "crampons" can be attached to them for climbing icy slopes.

These lightweight walking boots are just the job for general use. They're comfortable and flexible, but they still protect your feet and are reasonably waterproof. The sole is specially designed so that it doesn't clog with mud.

As much as 60 per cent of your body heat is lost through the top of your head. So, if it's cold wear a balaclava type hat. And, when it's hot and sunny, a hat will shade your eyes and help prevent heatstroke.

This kind of waterproof is often called a "shell garment" and will protect you from both wind and rain. Shell garments are often made from nylon for toughness, with a special backing for waterproofing. Of course, if your waterproof doesn't let the rain in, it may not let your sweat out either, but there is a range of good water-proofs that manage to do just that. Unfortunately, these tend to be horribly expensive.

If it's likely to be cold while you're out, take a woollen sweater or a good sweatshirt. Of course, if you have one, an anorak would be ideal. If you have the opportunity to buy a new one, go to a good outdoor shop for advice.

In very cold conditions, gloves or mittens are important. They now are made from many dif-ferent materials.

If it looks like rain, never wear jeans when out walking. They soak up water and soon become, heavy, clammy, and cold. There are all sorts of walking trousers available now in a variety of materials and colours, from heavyweight tweeds to light but windproof and quick-drying polycot-ton weaves.

   Of course, shorts are very comfortable if it's hot, but be careful not to let your legs get sun-burned or, if you are somewhere where you might come across stinging plants or animals, then trousers may still be better. Waterproof trousers, made of the same material as your shell garment, are well worth taking with you on a long hike.

Some people hate wearing waterproofs. If you do, try gaters, which protect the bottom parts of your legs from wet, mud, and cuts.

Back to the boots again.

TAKING THE WEIGHT

You'll need some kind of rucksack for your spare clothing and any other bits and pieces of equipment that you might need. Again, these can be very expensive and there is a huge variety of different types and sizes. You can even buy a rucksack which has been tailored to fit your own back length. Your local outdoor shop will be able to give you good advice on the best kind to buy, but it is as well to do some research first so that, at least, you know what you will be using it for and how much you are likely to be carrying in it. Will you just need a spare pair of socks, a waterproof, a sweater, and perhaps a bar of chocolate, or will you be carrying all you need for a week's backpacking in the hills, where there are no shops (or people)?

It may be that you can carry everything you are likely to need in the pockets of your clothing – but don't forget, these may not be waterproof. Then there are small daypacks or waistpacks. Mountaineers and rock climbers need rucksacks to carry all their gear in, but they have to be designed so that they fit snugly to the body, do not make them top (or bottom) heavy and are unlikely to get snagged in rock crevices. A full expedition sack might

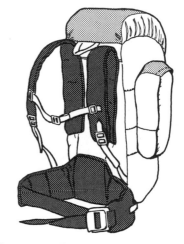

Left: *This popular rucksack has a harness system* (right) *which can be adjusted easily to fit the wearer's build comfortably.*

CHECKLIST

Remember to pack your rucksack with the heavier items at the top, especially for a longer expedition. So, starting from the bottom, you might include the following equipment:

- *sleeping bag and insulated mat*
- *emergency bag*
- *small first-aid kit*
- *extra warm clothing (if it is likely to become colder) or sunhat and shorts, for example*
- *waterproof clothing*
- *spare food*
- *cooking stove, pots, and pans (lightweight)*
- *whistle*
- *torch*
- *water and/or other drinks*
- *waterproof matches and spare fuel for stove*
- *lightweight tent*

There are other items you can add to suit your own needs, but try not to carry more than you need. Always remember to pack things so that you can get at them easily.

For a day's walk in the countryside, or even into wilder country, a full-size rucksack is likely to be too big. A smaller, lighter, but equally comfortable daypack is a much better bet.

have a pocket at the bottom, a main compartment, a pocket on the lid, and various pockets around the sides which may or may not be removeable. Sometimes, they also have special straps and loops for carrying things like ice axes.

Whatever kind of rucksack you're using, and whatever it's made from, it's not going to be 100 per cent waterproof, mainly because of the stitching. So, anything that you want to keep dry, such as spare clothing, should be kept in a plastic bag. Some people even line the whole of the inside of the sack with plastic bags.

You should also think about how you pack your rucksack. Obviously, things that you are likely to need quickly should be accessible but, on the other hand, it is a good idea to pack heavy things at the top, provided the items at the bottom will not get squashed. It is a good idea to practise packing your rucksack at home before you go to decide how heavy things are and how easy it is to get at the various bits of equipment. There's nothing worse than packing up everything you think you'll need, only to find you can't lift the sack – or stopping for lunch and having to take everything out of the pack to get at your sandwiches.

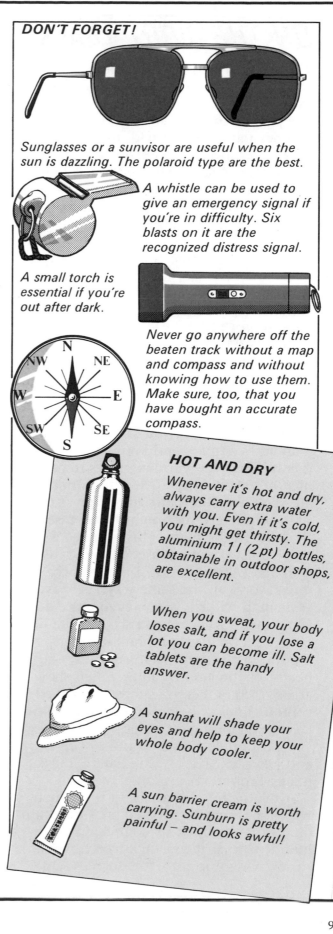

DON'T FORGET!

Sunglasses or a sunvisor are useful when the sun is dazzling. The polaroid type are the best.

A whistle can be used to give an emergency signal if you're in difficulty. Six blasts on it are the recognized distress signal.

A small torch is essential if you're out after dark.

Never go anywhere off the beaten track without a map and compass and without knowing how to use them. Make sure, too, that you have bought an accurate compass.

HOT AND DRY

Whenever it's hot and dry, always carry extra water with you. Even if it's cold, you might get thirsty. The aluminium 1 l (2 pt) bottles, obtainable in outdoor shops, are excellent.

When you sweat, your body loses salt, and if you lose a lot you can become ill. Salt tablets are the handy answer.

A sunhat will shade your eyes and help to keep your whole body cooler.

A sun barrier cream is worth carrying. Sunburn is pretty painful – and looks awful!

ON THE RIGHT TRACK

The minds of animals, including humans, are quite remarkable. Some birds, for example, newly emerged from the nest in one part of the world, are able to fly to another part of the world, thousands of kilometres away, where they might spend the winter. And all this without a map! It's thought that some birds, such as homing pigeons, even have a kind of built-in magnetic compass.

We're pretty good at finding our way around as well. Just think how many journeys you make without a map, simply because you've done the journey before, and you can remember the clues and the landmarks. Think of a journey that you know well, and then write down all the landmarks on that journey – road junctions, shops, a church, a factory, a special tree, and so on.

But, if you're going to strike out into unknown territory, you should have a map and compass and know how to use them. There are various points to remember about maps. Most important of all, they use different scales. For example, 1 km on the ground might be represented by 2 cm on the map. This is called a 1:50,000 scale and is a good one to use for walking. (A map worked out in inches and miles works in the same way.) A 1:25,000 scale map will show you even more detail. Most maps are arranged so that due north on the ground (geographic) is exactly to the top of the map. Maps indicate the height of the land by lines which show areas of equal height – these are called contour lines. They also use symbols to represent buildings, including churches and post offices; roads, railways, rivers, and lakes; car parks; woodland; crags; boggy ground and so on.

A magnetic compass is an instrument in which a pointer is pivoted on a fine point (and often damped by some kind of liquid) so that it can turn freely over a scale divided up into 360 degrees. One

end of the pointer, often coloured red, will always point to the Earth's magnetic north pole (in the northern hemisphere). Using a map and compass together, you can find your way around in places you don't know.

A good kind of compass to have is the "Silva" type. It comes with full instructions and you should read these and practise at home or in the park.

Triangulation (see diagram on page 94) can be worked out using a compass. Let's have a go.

Imagine you are on a footpath which you can see marked on the map, but you don't know how far along it you are. Choose a landmark in the distance, such as a mountain top or a church, that you can recognize on the map. Line up your compass with the landmark and turn the dial until the pointer lies north–south in the north–south rules on the compass. Next, place the compass on the map with

92

one edge on the landmark symbol. Align the edge of the compass, so that the north–south rules on the dial are in line with north–south on the map. The point where the edge of the compass crosses your path is how far along it you are. You can confirm this with one or more readings. But don't forget that magnetic north and geographic north are not the same (*see page 95*).

You must be able to use a map and compass properly if you are to venture into unknown or remote country. They can help you to work out exactly where you are and also to plot your route.

It is not always easy to relate what you see on the map to the countryside that you see around you. Firstly, it is a good idea to hold your map in such a way that the north on the map is in line with north on the ground. You can do this accurately with a compass or roughly by the position of the sun.

Lay the map out on the ground and line up the compass on it so that the 0° to 180° line of the compass is in line with magnetic north–south. Then turn the map so that magnetic north–south lines up with the north–south of the compass needle. On the facing page, you can see how to find north using the sun and a wristwatch.

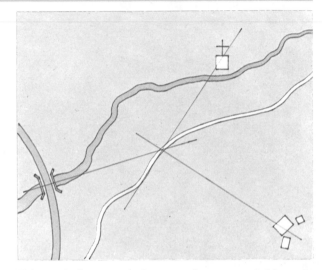

Triangulation can help you plot your position accurately.

Another useful way of setting the map and finding north at the same time (without using a compass) is to look for a feature on the ground, such as a railway

---

THE SILVA COMPASS

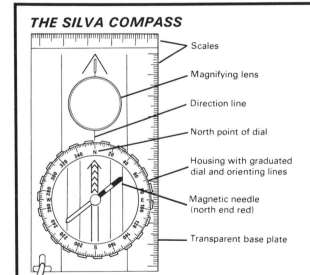

Scales
Magnifying lens
Direction line
North point of dial
Housing with graduated dial and orienting lines
Magnetic needle (north end red)
Transparent base plate

For most purposes, the "Silva" type compass is the best to buy. It is light to carry and accurate to about 1°. There are various kinds, ranging from simple and quite cheap versions, to more sophisticated and expensive ones. The basic compass consists of a transparent plastic base (marked with scales and a direction line) and a liquid-filled section containing the magnetic needle in which the red end points to magnetic north.

Taking a bearing

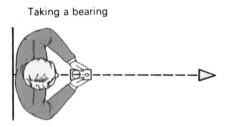

To take a bearing, hold the compass in front of you, so that the direction line points accurately at the object. Turn the housing of the compass so that the red end of the compass needle points to zero on the scale. The bearing of the object can be read off from the point where the direction line meets the scale on the compass.

Reading a bearing

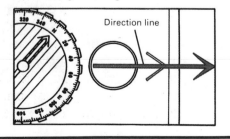

Direction line

TRUE NORTH

It is important to remember that the magnetic North Pole is not located at the geographic North Pole. The effect of this is that the direction of north indicated by a compass needle is not exactly the same as geographic north, nor the same as grid north on a map. Some compasses enable you automatically to allow for this but, if you do not have one of these compasses, then you must make a simple calculation yourself. Look at the illustration and you can see the angular differences between these "norths" in a country such as Britain. The angle between geographic north and magnetic north is called the *magnetic variation and is shown on most maps.*

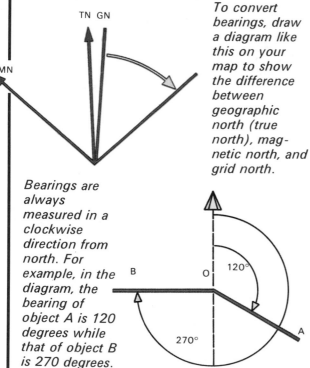

To convert bearings, draw a diagram like this on your map to show the difference between geographic north (true north), magnetic north, and grid north.

Bearings are always measured in a clockwise direction from north. For example, in the diagram, the bearing of object A is 120 degrees while that of object B is 270 degrees.

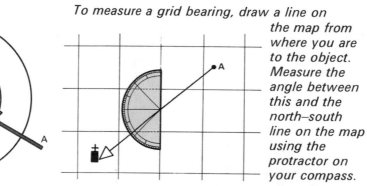

To find north in the northern hemisphere using a watch, turn the watch until the hour hand points towards the Sun. The line bisecting the angle between the hour hand and a line joining the centre of the watch to 12 o'clock points south. The opposite direction is north.

To measure a grid bearing, draw a line on the map from where you are to the object. Measure the angle between this and the north–south line on the map using the protractor on your compass.

line or road, a line of hills or a ridge. Then you can carefully line up the map with the feature you can see, and, of course, the north direction on the map will correspond with north on the ground. But remember, methods such as this can only give you *approximate* directions. If

you need to find your way more accurately, for example, if you are looking for a way down off a mountain, you will still need to use a compass.

Once you have set the map, you can compare features that you can see on the ground with those marked on the map.

SETTING UP CAMP

There are probably as many different ideas about good and bad tents and campsites as there are people who regularly camp out. There is certainly an immense variety of shapes and sizes of tents available for different purposes. They range widely in price and are made from different materials. Some are light, some heavy, some suitable for camping in the freezing conditions of the Antarctic,

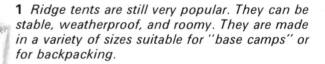

1 *Ridge tents are still very popular. They can be stable, weatherproof, and roomy. They are made in a variety of sizes suitable for "base camps" or for backpacking.*

2 *Tunnel tents are a comparatively recent innovation. For their weight and bulk, they can be roomy inside. Some people complain that heavy snow can accumulate on them and make them sag.*

3 *Wedge tents were once very common for lightweight camping. Pitched end-on into the wind they are very weatherproof. Also, because they are smaller at the foot end, they are lighter and less bulky than the equivalent ridge tent.*

Opposite: *if you can find some suitable poles, or a wall and some stones, and you have come prepared with a lightweight groundsheet, you can easily make a temporary shelter to escape the worst of the weather.*

4 *Dome-shaped tents with one or two sectional hoops for support are very roomy for their bulk and weight. Also, they offer more shoulder space* *for their height. Pitched properly, they are also very stable but good-quality tents of this type can be expensive to buy.*

while others are designed for use on safari where they need to be cool and insect-proof. There is even one type of tent which has been made, with a solid floor, and can be suspended from the side of mountains – occupants need to be careful when they leave it!

Take advice from magazines and from your outdoor retailers but, in the end, it will be your own experience which dictates to you the best kind of tent for your needs.

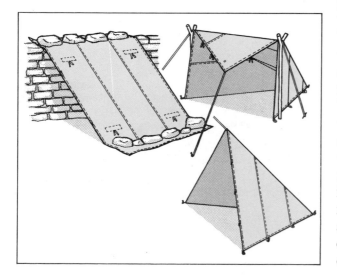

To start with, why not try a night under canvas (these days usually cotton or nylon) in your garden. Then, you need hardly spend a fortune on your first tent or you could even borrow one. Even if it rains, you can always sneak back to your warm, dry, comfortable bed! But this kind of experience does help to show you what you need from a tent.

With all the shapes and sizes available, it's hard to choose a good tent, but here are a few general guidelines. If you are going to camp where it might be cold, wet, and windy, your tent must obviously be waterproof. But, if it's completely waterproof, condensation might build up on the inside overnight and, when you move in the morning, you still get soaked! Your tent should also be stable when it's windy; tents have been known to blow away in the night, taking their occupants with them. It shouldn't flap because the noise will keep you awake. It should be fairly easy to pitch (especially useful if it's raining). It should be   enough for you and your gear and, if you are carrying it on your back, it should be light and compact.

SAFETY FIRST

To apply the kiss of life lie the person on the ground on his/her back. Make sure that the person's airway is clear. Kneel beside the head. Tilt the person's head back by pulling the chin upwards and the top of the head down. The victim may start breathing.

Pinch the nose shut and open the mouth. Take a full breath, place your mouth over the victim's mouth and breathe firmly into it. Repeat every four or five seconds. **Never practise on anyone, and do not use this method until you have been properly taught.**

 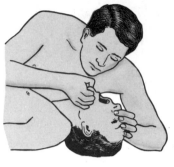 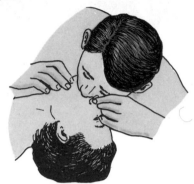

You would never cross the road without looking carefully in both directions at least once to make sure that it is clear. But it is surprising how many people venture into remote and possibly hostile countryside without the right equipment and without knowing how to cope. However experienced you are, you should never travel alone in wild country. It is better to be in a party of at least three people so that, in the event of an injury, for example, one person can go for help while one stays with the victim to keep him/her warm (or cool) and comfortable. And young people should always be accompanied by an adult if they're going into any rugged landscape.

The pictures above show some basic first-aid actions. But do not use any of them until you have been properly taught. Basically, the three most important life-threatening circumstances to look for are: is the victim breathing; is the heart functioning normally; is the victim bleeding? Broken bones come next, and then any more minor problems. At the same time, you should make sure that you and everyone else keeps calm and that neither you nor the victim is likely to be in any further danger.

Never go off on a trip into the hills, or anywhere else where there could be risk, without telling someone where you are going. At least if you have left information about your plans, then, if an emergency does occur, time is not lost in trying to find out where you were going and whether or not you have enough food to last you until the next day. Don't forget that in an emergency, a torch or whistle can be used to signal for help (six

Always carry a simple first-aid kit with you. It could contain the following items: a selection of adhesive plasters; wound dressings; stretch bandages; triangular bandages; insect repellent and bite cream; antiseptic cream; some cotton wool; a small pair of scissors; needle and thread; salt tablets and barrier cream (useful in a hot climate).

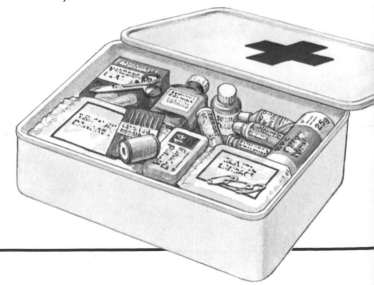

1 *You can check someone's pulse by feeling for the artery as shown.*

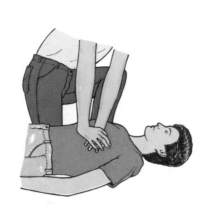

3 *The quickest way to stop bleeding is to apply firm pressure to the wound with your hand.* **Do not apply a tourniquet.**

2 *If someone's heart has stopped beating, it is possible to start it up again by heart massage.* **Never practise on anyone. Do not use this method until you have been properly taught.**

4 *This is the best position for someone to be in to recover from a serious condition. It is called the recovery position.* **Do not try to move anyone who may have damage to the back.**

long blasts on the whistle or six flashes of the torch).

It's a good idea to leave an information card with a responsible person before you set off. This is what you should include:
- Name, address, and phone number
- Responsible guardian or parent to contact
- Local address and contact
- Number of people in the party
- Time of departure and return
- Route and destinations
- Length of route
- Emergency equipment and spare food

IN AN EMERGENCY

What do you do if the worst comes to the worst, and you are stuck on a mountain with worsening weather and night falling? You should be properly prepared but remember if night falls and you can't see where you're going, stay put, if there's any danger of falling. Try to find a way to shelter from the worst of the weather.

If there's deep snow, you can protect yourself from wind chill by digging a snowhole and crawling inside. Or try sheltering from driving wind behind a wall.

Huddle together out of the wind for warmth.

Even a solitary tree can give some shade.

SPECIAL EQUIPMENT

"Environment" is a much used word today. This is because all over the world we have come to realize that man does not live alone, but in delicate balance with the wild animals and plants of the natural world. We need to learn about nature for our own survival. Nature is not dull. Things are happening around us all the time. Even if you spent your whole life studying nature you could never hope to know everything, so there is plenty of room for amateur naturalists to make their own studies. Many important discoveries have been found by amateurs.

This book will help you find out how nature works. Not only by reading about it, but by doing really interesting projects.

Most of the basic equipment you will need is cheap and easy to obtain.

A nature table should be strong enough to support the weight of your aquarium and big enough to allow you to sort out the masses of shells and seaweeds, bones and caterpillars that you are bound to collect as you become more and more interested. If you haven't got room for a whole table a nature shelf will do fine, and a piece of soft board on the wall behind will display some of your collection splendidly.

A notebook with a pencil attached should be always in your pocket. This is to jot down casual observations in the field. It's no good trying to remember things when you get home. Try to make a few rough drawings as well. You can keep a proper *Nature diary* on the nature table in which you write up your findings and make more careful illustrations. It's a good idea to use maps and photographs if you can. This adds a really professional touch!

pooter

fixative

Hides or blinds are useful for observation and photography. You can make a simple hide out of greenish brown cotton or canvas stretched over a frame of sticks

A hand lens or magnifying glass is indispensable to real nature watchers. Use one to take a look at the detail of a butterfly's wing or the sting of a nettle or a wasp.

Binoculars are absolutely necessary for birdwatching; 8 × 30 magnification is ideal to start with.

A good torch is invaluable for night-time explorations.

A fishing net for pond dipping can be made with a circle of stiff wire attached to a long pole and covered with netting, or cheap ones are easily available. For catching very small aquatic animals you can attach a plastic container to the bottom of the net.

You will need lots of containers – boxes, small tins, saucers and other containers, in which to carry your discoveries home. Fungi, flowers and feathers are very fragile. Each needs a special travelling box. You will need a plastic bucket with a lid for expeditions to the stream. Try begging one from your local delicatessen or supermarket. And don't forget your rubber boots!

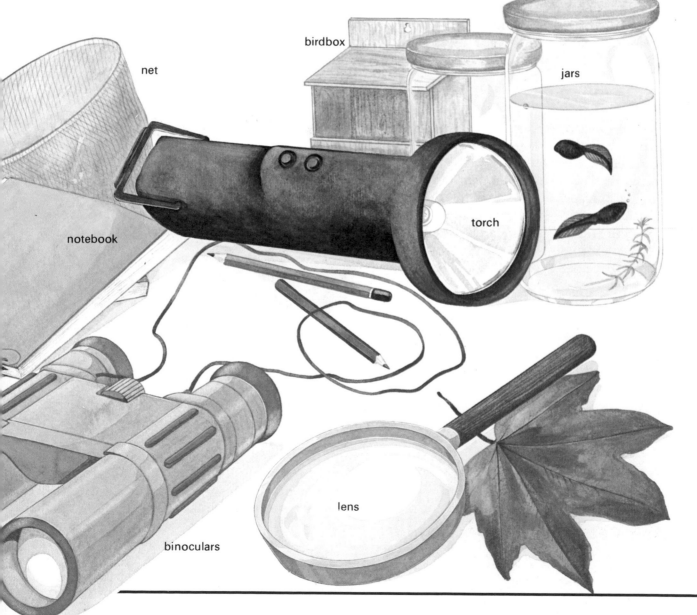

net

birdbox

jars

notebook

torch

lens

binoculars

THE CONSERVATION PATCH

A conservation patch is a good place to study wildlife. A corner of the garden, a piece of rough ground, even a city windowbox can attract wildlife to it. Think of your conservation patch as an animal café and rest area. If you plant the right flowers and establish the right kind of shelter, wild guests of all kinds will move in.

Save the weeds Some weeds attract insects. Butterflies will suck nectar from the flowers. The peacock, the red admiral and the small tortoiseshell lay their eggs on nettles. When the eggs hatch out the caterpillars feed on the leaves.

Plant a hedge if you can. If you have one already, you will notice that it provides shelter and that birds like to feed and nest in it.

Many garden flowers are good for wildlife. The buddlea bush and the ice plant will attract butterflies from miles around.

Bee borage Perhaps you only have a window box or a small patch. You can grow bee borage.

1 Get a packet of borage seeds and sprinkle them on a layer of seed compost or clean soil laid out in a tray. Cover the seeds with a thin layer of compost or soil and water well.

2 Place the tray in a large polythene bag on a windowsill until the seeds have germinated. Water occasionally so the soil doesn't dry out.

3 When your seeds have sprouted into tiny seedlings, remove the polythene bag.

4 When the tiny borage plants have grown a few leaves you can transplant them into a windowbox, or a large plant pot for the patio, or directly into the soil in your conservation patch if the weather is warm.

Many butterflies as well as bees will visit your borage wherever it is.

A bundle of drinking straws held together with sticky tape can be pinned underneath a windowbox or windowsill. Small bees and wasps will nest inside. Brightly coloured straws will attract the insects.

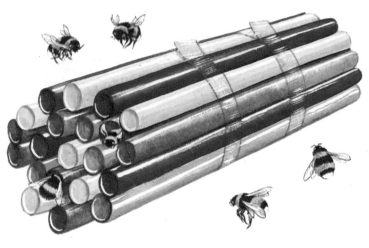

Leave a few large stones around for invertebrates to hide under. In many countries this is where scorpions rest during the heat of the day. It is also a popular woodlice retreat. How many kinds can you find?

Make a pile of logs This acts as a hotel for many small animals. If you build a really big pile you may attract a fox, even in a city. Out in the country, log piles left near streams may shelter mink and otters.

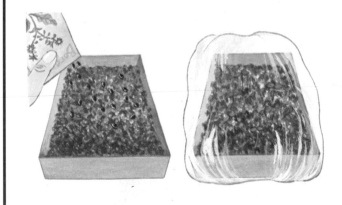

MAKE A SNAIL ROOST

Make a snail roost by leaving broken flowerpots in your dampest area. Snails travel about at night looking for food and sleep in shady places during the day. If you mark the shell with dabs of paint you can identify your snail when you see it again.

Water is important to all animals. If you provide some, many creatures will come to your conservation patch to drink.

- A bird bath can be made from an old meat tray. You'll get hours of fun watching the birds queuing up to bathe.
- Dig a pond, if there's room. A piece of heavy duty plastic will contain the water but be careful not to get holes in it. You can grow rushes and other waterplants round the edge. Bats and insect-eating birds like to feed near water in the evening. Many animals will come to drink and feed there.

Build a hedgehog house for hedgehogs to hibernate in.

1 Fill a wooden box with straw and cover it over with heavy plastic.
2 Make a hole in the side of the box and attach a large piece of pipe to it, to act as a tunnel. This will keep predators out.
3 Encourage hedgehogs by leaving a saucerful of milk out each night. You may also get other animals coming to feed.

POND DIPPING

Pond dipping is great fun and you always find something exciting. Take a net and some containers to put your finds in. You'll also need a hand lens to examine them. Don't forget your rubber boots. Tell an adult where you are going.

Creep up quietly to the stream or pond. There may be birds like herons fishing there already, or fish basking.

First of all, pass your net along the surface of the water. Here you'll find pondskaters and whirling beetles as well as mosquito larvae. There are flatworms up here as well as in the mud. Now swish the net through the water weeds. This is where the snails live. Lastly, check out the bottom. Here you will find caddis fly larvae and tubifex worms too.

You can take your finds home to keep in a bucket for a few days, but the best idea is to set up a proper aquarium. Take home a large container of water rich in microscopic life.

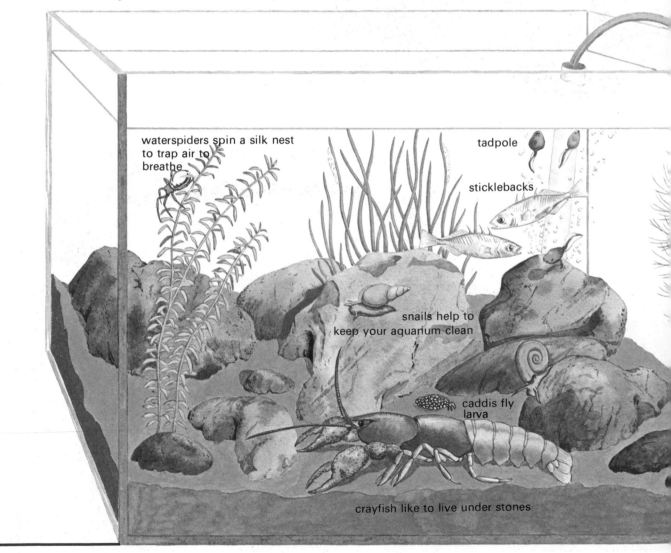

waterspiders spin a silk nest to trap air to breathe

tadpole

sticklebacks

snails help to keep your aquarium clean

caddis fly larva

crayfish like to live under stones

SETTING UP A FRESHWATER AQUARIUM

1 A glass aquarium can be bought from a petshop, together with the various accessories you need to make the filtration system work.

2 Put the aquarium on a solid table. When it is full of water it will be very heavy and difficult to move. Don't put it on a windowsill or in direct sunlight.

3 It is not necessary to use a filter at all if you are prepared to change the water every few days. But if you want to keep your aquatic creatures for a long time, then a filter is the best way to keep the water clean and the animals healthy.

4 At the bottom of the aquarium place your plastic undergravel filter. Attach the filter tube at one end, placing it towards the back of the tank so that it can be hidden by rocks and weed. Attach a length of airpipe to your airstone and lower it down the pipe. Then attach the other end of the airpipe to a 2-way gang valve which you attach to the side of the aquarium. A second airpipe is used to connect this valve to the electrically driven airpump.

5 You can sterilize the gravel properly by putting it in the oven in an old baking tin for half an hour at a reasonably high temperature. Let it cool before putting it in the aquarium.

6 Smooth the gravel over the filter, banking it up a bit towards the back. Then place some attractive rocks in the tank. This is not just decoration but shelter for the fish and something for them to graze over. Plant some weeds in the gravel. Then pour water gently into the aquarium.

7 Place a cover over the tank to keep out dust. Let the water settle for 24 hours before putting animals in.

AQUARIUM STARS

Tiny creatures need to be looked at with a magnifying glass or hand lens. Put them in a shallow dish to get the best view. Or you could make *a viewing chamber*. Take two pieces of glass and place a rubber tube in a U shape between them. Now clip the glass together with two large bulldog clips. You can pour a little water into the U between the glass pieces and drop in the creature you want to examine.

Remember that many animals are carnivorous and may eat each other. Beware particularly of the great diving beetle which will eat prey many times its own size. If in doubt, keep your animal in a separate container for a few days until you work out its habits.

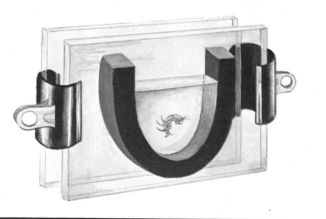

THE SEASHORE

At the seashore, what you do depends on whether the tide is in or out. It's just the same for the animals that live there. Underwater a limpet is able to move around the rock grazing on algae. When the tide goes out it must withdraw into its shell and stick hard to the rockface to protect itself from battering waves, hot sunshine and hungry birds.

Find out what a limpet does underwater by marking its shell and the spot you found it in, with nail varnish. At low tide move it to another rock. Next day you will find it has returned to its first home.

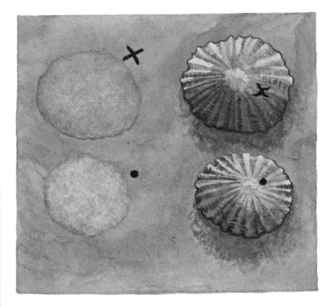

Watch underwater creatures through a diving mask. You can lie on the rocks with your head in the water of a rockpool. Or you can take a look at the seabed.

MAKE A VIEWING BOX TO SEE UNDERWATER

1 Take a large plastic box or bowl and cut a hole in the bottom. Leave a lip.
2 Now glue a piece of glass or perspex over the hole. Use a strong glue or silicon cement. Cling film will do if you carry it right up over the sides of the box and secure it at the top.
3 Now you can use your box to see underwater without getting wet.

FISHWATCH

Fish often get stranded in rock pools. If you wear polaroid sunglasses to cut out reflected light and sit very quietly you can easily study them. You may see young flatfish if you move a stick vigorously in a sandy pool. These fish (dabs, flounders, plaice and sole) breed just offshore. To begin with, a flatfish isn't flat, and it has eyes on both sides of its head. But as it adopts a bottom dwelling life, its eyes gradually move to the top.

DANGER FISH

If you live in the tropics you should always wear shoes when searching rock pools. There are several marine organisms that could severely hurt you. Stonefish and certain jellyfish can be dangerous. Check with an adult who knows the area and its wildlife well.

SEAWEEDS

Seaweeds are marine algae. Each type of seaweed is particular to a certain part of the shore. Here are a few common ones.

At the top of the beach grow the green **sea lettuce**, **grass kelp** and **sea moss**.

In the middle zone you usually find brown seaweeds. **Channelled wrack** is the first of these. It rolls up its fronds to prevent itself from drying out. You will also find **flat wracks** and on rough, exposed beaches masses of **bladder wrack.**

Lower down, in deep, dark pools you will notice various types of red seaweed. **Red laver** is good to eat.

SEAWEED PRESSING

You can press seaweeds to make a collection, rather like you press flowers.

1 Arrange the seaweed in a bowl of water.
2 Slide white paper under it and lift it all out on to a pile of newspapers.
3 Cover with muslin and another layer of newspapers. Place a book on top. Not a heavy weight or the seaweed will get stuck to the newspaper.
4 While the seaweed is wet, change the newspaper every day.

EBB AND FLOW

The moon influences the tides. Twice a month – when the moon is full and when it is new – there are big tides. More of the beach is exposed at low tide on these days. It is then that you will find kelps and thongweeds growing on the rocks. If you look amongst the Holdfasts, which are the discs or rootlike branches that attach the seaweed to the rocks, you will find mussels, sea urchins and swimming crabs.

Do watch out when exploring an isolated shoreline that you don't get cut off by the incoming sea. It's very easy to forget the time when there are lots of fascinating items to collect.

BIRDWATCHING 1

Binoculars are essential for a birdwatcher. With them, distant black dots take on identifiable colours and shapes – without them, they remain just black dots! Prices vary greatly, but a reasonable pair can be bought quite cheaply. Go to a good local shop to try them out before buying, because they must be easy and comfortable for *you* to use.

Real enthusiasts will find a telescope most useful in places such as estuaries, large lakes and reservoirs, particularly when they are looking at ducks, geese and waders. This is because the telescope's magnification is that much greater, and in these areas you usually remain at some distance from the birds you are watching. A pocket-sized "field guide" identification book is very helpful, but remember always to make your own notes and sketches of the birds as you saw them, with details of date, place and weather conditions.

Left: *Binoculars with ×8 or ×9 magnification are suitable for most habitats. It is sometimes better to use ×10 by the sea, but remember that these will be heavier.*

Left: *A good telescope gives superb views of distant birds, and a tripod is essential to keep it steady. Unfortunately both are expensive.*

Above: *Using a telescope well takes practice, but the rewards are great.*

DO'S AND DON'TS OF BIRDWATCHING

√ keep alert
√ take time to stop look and listen

× hurry
× make a loud or sudden noise
× wear bright clothing

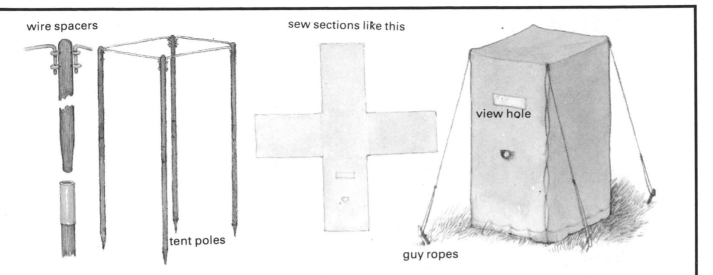

wire spacers

sew sections like this

tent poles

view hole

guy ropes

APPROACHING BIRDS

Of all animals, birds are often the most alert and wary. The rule when birdwatching is therefore to do your best to see the bird before it sees you. A stealthy approach is needed, moving quietly, with frequent pauses to **listen** – birds can often be heard singing or calling long before you catch sight of them.

Take a route that keeps you in the shelter of nearby bushes if you are out in the open, and never walk along the top of a bank or sea wall. Keep below the skyline, putting your head up cautiously every so often to check what is there. Another technique is to use a hide – but remember that you must not disturb the birds, for their sake, and that nesting birds are protected by law.

MAKING A HIDE

A portable hide is really a small square tent, usually of canvas or camouflage material, with an observation slit in one or more sides. Tent poles and stiff wire spacers make a sturdy frame, over which the canvas cover fits. The cover should be sewn together as a cross. The entrance flap and observation slit are closed with zips or "velcro" fastenings. The tent is kept in position by guy ropes and tent pegs hold the canvas down to prevent flapping.

The hide should be small enough to be easily carried, but large enough to take you, a seat (an absolute must, or you will move to ease a stiff leg and disturb the birds), your binoculars and perhaps a tripod and camera or telescope.

Above: *Hides are not difficult to make – or you could buy one. Don't forget that cars make good "hides" for bird watching.*

Right: *Ringing birds, to monitor their movements, is rewarding work. Join a local birdwatching society, and you may be able to take part.*

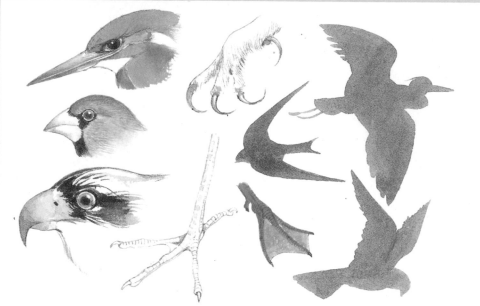

Left: *Look for and note down any distinguishing features of the birds you see, as you see them. The size, colour and shape of wings, beak and feet will all help to identify them later. They will also give you a lot of clues about the birds, particularly about their feeding habits.*

Below: *Note carefully how the birds you have spotted fly. Straight, swooping, soaring or hovering flight patterns will help in identification.*

Birds have a number of features that help them survive in their chosen habitat, and these characteristics will help you sort out just what group the bird belongs to. Good examples are the powerful hooked beaks of the birds of prey, the dagger-like beaks of herons and the kingfisher, the webbed feet of ducks and geese and the longer legs of herons and waders. Seed-eaters (such as finches) have short, stout, triangular beaks, while fruit and insect-eaters (thrushes and warblers) have medium-length slim beaks. Birds of the open skies, such as the swift, have long slender wings, while woodland birds, such as the dove, have short wings.

Below: *Note down as much as you can about any birds you see while you are out. A few rough drawings will help, too. Details are easily forgotten once you get home!*

25th June
dark wing
long beak
light breast

- Britain's longest-haul migrant is the Arctic tern. It breeds in the Arctic but flies south to winter off the Antarctic ice-cap, a round trip of about 30,000 kilometres.

- At around 35 kilograms, the mute swan (Britain's heaviest bird) is about 7,000 times heavier than the 5 gram goldcrest, the lightest.

- Britain's commonest nesting birds are the house sparrow, starling and chaffinch. There are more than 5 million pairs of each at peak times.

- Britain's rarest bird is the snowy owl. Since 1983 7 females have been sighted, but no males.

Above: *Most estuary birds have to probe deep into the mudflats at low tide for worms and shellfish, so many have long beaks. They usually have long legs (so that they don't get wet!) and all have long toes to stop them sinking into the mud.*

USING FIELD GUIDES

In field guides, birds are often grouped in families of related species (ducks, hawks, waders, and so on). Once you have checked a bird's distinguishing features, such as beak, legs and feet, you will be able to work out which family you think it belongs to. Then you can turn to the group of illustrations to see which bird best fits your notes.

Some guides are designed for use only in one habitat – woodland or marshland for example. This can be helpful, as it greatly

reduces the possibilities of confusion, but never forget that birds fly between habitats or have a wide habitat choice. "Sea" gulls, for example, may commonly be found on a grassy field.

As you go birdwatching through the different seasons of the year and you visit new habitats, you will build up a store of useful identification features that help you take short-cuts. The way a bird moves or flies (called its *jizz*) may tell you more than the colours of its feathers, and more quickly. Songs and calls, too, are not only enjoyable to listen to, but useful aids to identification. Again, experience helps greatly, but you can learn a great deal by listening to the tapes or records of bird song now readily available. Try your local library.

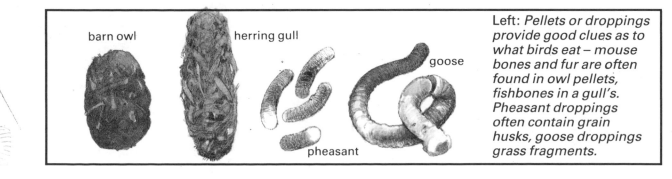

barn owl   herring gull   goose

pheasant

Left: *Pellets or droppings provide good clues as to what birds eat – mouse bones and fur are often found in owl pellets, fishbones in a gull's. Pheasant droppings often contain grain husks, goose droppings grass fragments.*

CATCHING INSECTS

MAKE A LARGE SWEEP NET

1 Take a piece of wire or a metal coat-hanger and twist it into a circle. Twist the loose ends together and attach them to a stick with a second piece of wire.

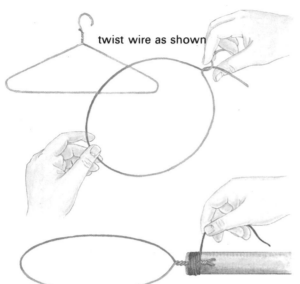

twist wire as shown

bind wire onto handle

thread net onto frame

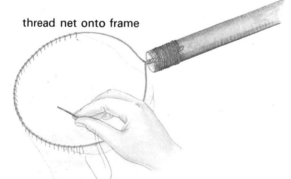

2 Make a cotton bag and attach this to the wire.
3 In an area of long grass, gently sweep the net to and fro. You should find many insects including caterpillars and pupae of various butterflies and moths.

4 Turn these out on to a white dish or cloth to examine.

Butterflies and moths have four stages in their lives. This is because an insect's skeleton is outside its body. It is a tough case of chiton. This protects the adult insect but does not allow it to grow. So in the early stage of its life as a caterpillar it is able to shed its skin from time to time.

KEEPING CATERPILLARS

1 You can keep caterpillars in a plastic box. An ice cream container is ideal.
2 Prick a few small holes in the top and place paper in the bottom. This will keep the humidity right.
3 Your caterpillar will need daily fresh food and a clean cage. Give it leaves from the plant on which you found it.
4 Now you can watch your caterpillar grow. It will split its skin several times and turn into a pupa (chrysalis). Put a twig in the box for it to hang from.
5 The pupa does not feed. During this period the insect is reorganizing all its cells into the shape of the adult insect. It often does this during the winter months so keep your box cool.
6 At last the adult insect emerges. It will want to feed on nectar, so you should release it near flowers.

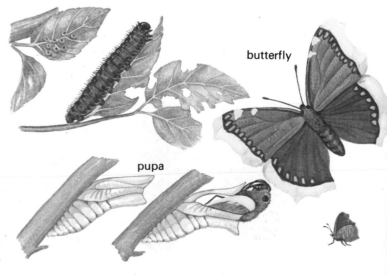

butterfly

pupa

CATCHING MOTHS WITH A LIGHT TRAP AT NIGHT

1 Tie a sheet from some branches of a tree during a period of warm weather.
2 Set up a bright electric torch so that the beam falls on the white fabric.
3 Many insects will be drawn to the light. Catch and examine them in a wide jar.

MAKE A POOTER

You will need: a length of pipe ● 2 rubber bungs with holes through them ● a glass tube.

Many insects are too small to handle easily, and a pooter will enable you to pick them up without hurting them.
1 Cut the pipe into two short lengths. Push them through the bungs and put the bungs into each end of the tube.
2 Now you can suck up the insect into the tube to transfer it from one place to another.

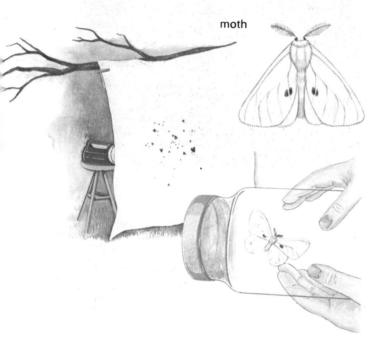

moth

You can keep some of your finds under a **gauze meat cover** placed on a wide tray. This is normally used for keeping insects out, but it is also excellent for keeping them in.

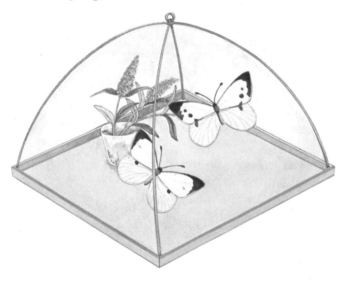

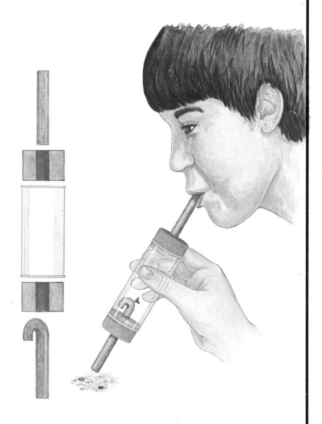

Use your pooter to collect ladybirds

Ladybirds are fun to keep and you can get them to lay eggs if you keep their cage absolutely clean and give them plenty of their favourite food, the aphid. Both adults and grubs eat a lot of aphids every day. The grubs will pupate for a week before turning into adult ladybirds.

MAMMALS

Mammals are animals which suckle their young. Many mammals will be very familiar to you either because you see them every day like dogs, horses, cats and sheep, or because you have seen them in wildlife programmes on television or in safari parks or zoos, like lions, tigers, elephants, giraffes and so on.

But some mammals are very shy and there are many mammals living near you that you will seldom see, such as mice and voles.

Some mammals are nocturnal, that is they only appear at night and sleep during the day. If you are very careful, still and quiet, it is sometimes possible to see a nocturnal mammal like a badger or a hedgehog or more often a fox.

Sometimes you can see which animals have passed by, by indentifying their footprints in snow or mud. There are other ways, too, of knowing when a mammal is around.

fur on wire

hole in hedge

nest hole

burrow

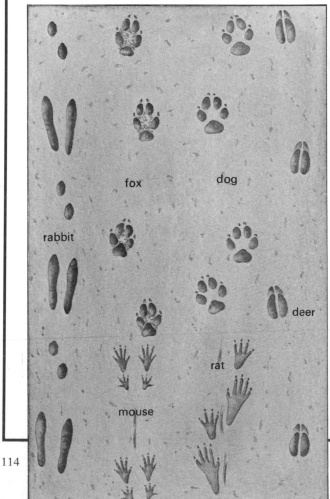

fox

dog

rabbit

deer

rat

mouse

If you take an old sheet of corrugated iron and leave it flat on the soil for a few months you will find that many animals will set up home underneath it. Watch out in countries where there are poisonous snakes though! That's just the kind of place they like to hide.

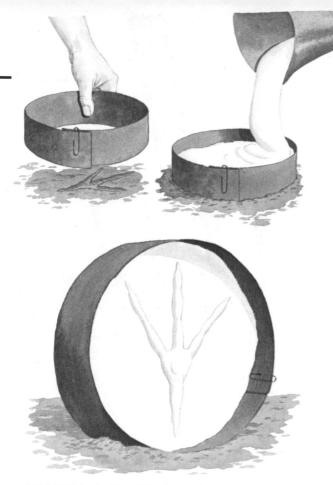

MAKING A PLASTER CAST

You will need: cardboard strip 30 cm (11¾ in) ×5 cm (2 in) ● paper clips ● trowel ● plastic bowl ● spoon ● newspapers.

Along the bed of a shallow stream there are muddy places where birds and animals have left tracks. Try to to make a plaster cast of some.

1 Clip your cardboard into a circle and place it over the track into the mud.
2 Mix plaster of Paris with clean stream-water and pour the mixture into the mould.
3 Plaster of Paris sets very quickly. You should be able to dig up the plaster cast after about fifteen minutes. Leave the cardboard round it. Wrap it all up in newspaper before carrying it.

VARIETY IS THE SPICE OF LIFE
There are so many different mammals it is hard to believe they have anything in common. Here are a few of them.

RECONSTRUCTING A SKELETON

It's a real challenge to reconstruct a skeleton! You may find a dead rabbit or you could try a mouse.

1 Attach string to its leg and bury it, so that one end of the string is visible and you can find the burial place again.
2 Leave for several weeks until there is no flesh left on the bones.
3 Dig up the skeleton with great care, gently brushing debris from the bones.
4 Carefully glue the bones together or attach with thin wire. Try to find a picture of the skeleton to guide you.

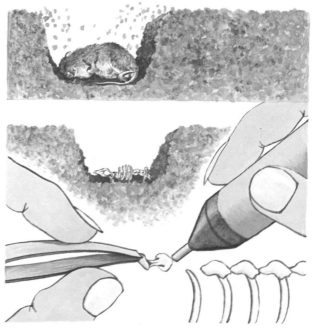

THE SOIL

If you dig down through the soil you will notice several layers. At the top is the leaf litter. This is rich in dying plant material and here you find many different kinds of mites feeding. Ants and spiders hunt here. As you turn the soil over you may find the pupae of moths and other insects. It is interesting to look under stones. Sometimes you find frogs, toads and newts buried in their chamber homes. Small mammals like voles and shrews make nests in the earth.

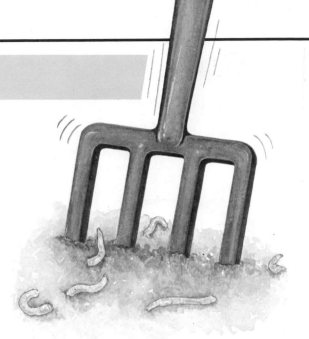

MAKE A WORMERY

You will need: 2 pieces of perspex ● 3 pieces of wood ● screws

1 Collect the worms. Banging a fork, stuck in the ground, will attract worms.
2 Fill the wormery with layers of different soils. You could put a layer of washed sand or gravel, mud from a stream, lighter soil from a hilltop.
3 Place a layer of leaves on top. Then install the worms. If you keep the wormery dark and moist the worms will be very comfortable.

Did you know that there are thousands of different sorts of worms? Many of them live in the soil, but others live in ponds, ditches and streams. Many live in the sea. The biggest earthworm comes from Australia and is over 3 m ($3\frac{1}{4}$ yd) long. There are over three thousand different types of earthworm. If you walk across a lawn on a warm, damp night you will find earthworms coming to the surface to look for food or to mate. Earthworms are hermaphrodites which means they are

If a perspex wormery is too expensive, you can use a jam jar. Fill it with layers of different soils and place leaves on top. Wrap dark paper around the jar, so that the worms will come to the sides.

Remember to keep the wormery dark and moist.

SOIL LAYER JAR

You will need: a milk bottle or jar • a plastic funnel • cotton wool • a jam jar • sand • clay • water • soil.

1 Place about 4 cm (1½ in) of soil in a jar or milk bottle.
2 Fill three-quarters full of water. Shake vigorously.
3 Leave to settle. Soil will have separated into distinct layers. The heaviest particles will be on the bottom and the lightest ones nearest the top.

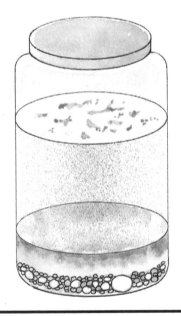

1 Dig a hole in the soil to fit your tin or jar.
2 Place the bricks on either side of the hole with the wood over the top.
3 Place some food at the bottom of the jar to attract small animals.
4 When you have caught something, pick up the whole container and empty it into a cotton bag, if you are taking your animal home.
5 The best place to keep small mammals is a purpose made box with plenty of ventilation. However, for a short time you could use a vivarium that is converted from an old aquarium.
6 When you have finished watching your animal, release it in the place you caught it, so it can go home.

both male and female. When they have mated with each other, both worms will make a cocoon full of eggs which they will leave to develop in the soil. After a few weeks one or two fully formed young worms will hatch out.

Worms are very good for the soil because they aerate it with their burrows. Their digging mixes the upper humus layers of the soil which are rich in fallen leaves and nutrients, with the poorer, stonier subsoil beneath.

A PITFALL TRAP

You will need: a large, deep tin or jar with smooth sides • four bricks • large piece of wood.

This can be very successful in catching small animals of all kinds.

HUNGRY FUNGI

Some fungi eat tiny animals in the soil. They are able to capture amoeba, which get stuck on sticky parts of the thread-like underground hypha. Some fungi produce a substance that sets like instant glue when microscopic worms or mites pass by. Fungi even set traps for their prey.

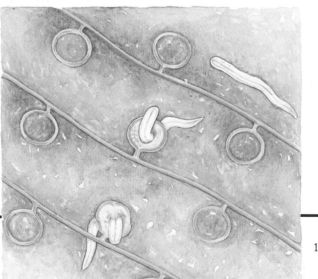

FUNGI

Fungi are vital to life on earth because they recycle the nourishing parts from dying things. You see a lot of mushrooms and toadstools in autumn when the leaves drop off the trees and there is plenty for them to feed on. If you shake a toadstool on to a piece of white paper you will see powdery spores drop out. Each of these spores can turn into another fungus. Sometimes the wind spreads spores, and sometimes insects help.

The **stinkhorn fungus** is very smelly. It smells so bad you can track it down in an autumn wood by its odour alone. Flies are drawn to it to feed on its slime so, of course, they pick up spores as well. A single speck of fly excrement may contain millions of stinkhorn fungus spores. They can grow into new fungi. So why aren't there stinkhorn fungi everywhere? The reason must be that fungi are very choosy about the places they grow. There are all sorts of different fungi, pushing billions of spores into the air. Fortunately for us, only a few of these spores will land in a place where they can develop.

Fungi like the **edible mushroom** and the **puffball** prefer grassy meadows. Others, like the **fly agaric** (above), will only grow in birch woods, feeding on fallen leaves. The **Jew's Ear fungus** is rarely found anywhere but on the trunks of fallen elder trees. The **mildew** that you sometimes find creating a blue-grey "dusty" effect on rose leaves is a fungus. So are the "rots" that kill seedlings and eat away at ripe fruit. Green apples are more resistant to fungi because their skin is waxier, and the rainborne spores cannot penetrate it.

Not only do we eat certain types of mushroom, but we use yeasts, to ferment our wine and beer and to make our bread rise. Penicillin, which grows as a mould, is a fungus too. We also use moulds in cheese making.

HOW TO MAKE A SPORE PRINT
1 Cut the stalk from the cap and discard.
2 Place the cap on paper and cover it with a bowl for a few hours.
3 Remove cap and spray fixative on the spore print from above so the jet of air does not disturb the spores.

PRESERVE A FUNGI USING HOT SAND
Place your fungi in a tin tray then heat up a quantity of sand in the oven and pour it over your fungi. Use gloves so you don't get burnt. Leave to cool before removing.

DIFFERENT MOULDS
1 Take an orange and a piece of bread.
2 Put them on different plates and place them in warm, moist places in your house. You could put one in the bathroom and another in the kitchen.
3 Do they grow the same mould?
4 If they grow different moulds, try the experiment again but swap the places round.

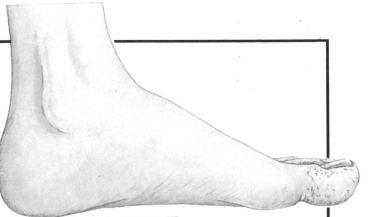

Some fungi grow on us. Athlete's foot is a sore that you often pick up in swimming pools. The fish in your aquarium may develop fungal diseases like fin rot. Whilst most of these fungal activities are just a nuisance, some of them can kill.

Changing the landscape The activities of fungi can change the landscape. Many serious tree diseases are caused by fungi. The English countryside looks very different today, compared with twenty years ago, because Dutch Elm Disease has killed more than 11 million trees. In North America oaks suffer from Oak Wilt and in Europe the beech is threatened by Beech Bark Disease. Insects spread the spores of the fungi and high winds also contribute.

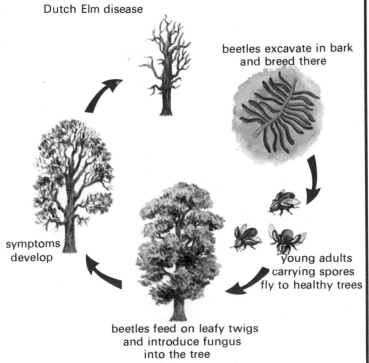

Dutch Elm disease

beetles excavate in bark and breed there

young adults carrying spores fly to healthy trees

beetles feed on leafy twigs and introduce fungus into the tree

symptoms develop

LOOKING AT FLOWERS

There is little in the world of nature to rival the beauty of an old meadow, rich in flowering plants in full bloom in midsummer. Sadly, today's farming technology makes such a sight more and more rare over much of Britain and Europe, except on the poor farming lands of the west and in Alpine meadows.

If you look at a meadow full of flowers you will be struck by a kaleidoscope of patterns, shapes and colours. But a hand lens will allow you to see many finer points of detail, so that you can identify each flower correctly. Flower field guides are sometimes arranged by colour, but more often by family. A little experience will allow you to place an unknown plant in, for example, the pea family, or the roses, or the "umbellifers" (wild carrot, hogweed and so on, with umbrella-shaped flower heads) because of its flower shape. Once you have been able to work out which family a flower belongs to, it is then not hard to identify the species.

Above: *Flowers spend their lives producing seeds. These seeds are very important, for they are the beginnings of new plants. They are spread out or scattered in four main ways: they are shot out by the parent plants, or are carried away by wind, water or animals. A wide variety of insects are used of which the bees and flies are the best known. Besides their bright, insect-attracting colours, some flowers also have a supply of sugar-rich nectar, that bees turn into honey.*

1

2

3

HOW FLOWERS REPRODUCE

Flowering plants reproduce by means of seeds. Some may be blown long distances, as in the case of the downy "parachutes" of thistles. The musk or monkey-flower seed pod explodes violently when touched, scattering seeds far and wide. The well-named cleavers have hooked seeds that cling to animal fur (and human clothing!) while the wild rose and yew have tempting berries that birds eat, the seeds passing out in their droppings later – and far away.

Left: *Heather (1) indicates peaty soil, bee orchids (2) chalky soil and herb Paris (3) ancient woodland.*

Right: *Hedgerows are often rich in flowers – they are the last refuge of the plants that used to grow in the meadows.*

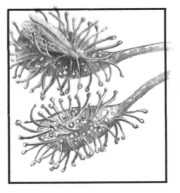

Above: *Some plants are carnivorous (meat-eaters). This sundew traps passing insects on its sticky leaves and digests them to obtain vital food.*

WHERE PLANTS LIVE

Plants can tell us a great deal about the habitat in which they are found. The presence of some may suggest the possibility of other plants that enjoy similar conditions. Heather (or ling) for example, is typical of damp, peaty moorland soils that are acid in nature. In contrast, many orchids, such as the bee orchid favour chalky soils. (The flower of this particular orchid looks just like a bee and attracts male pollinator bees, which believe they have found a mate!) Herb Paris also grows in chalky soil, and its presence tells you that you are in very old woodland.

AMPHIBIANS AND REPTILES

There are relatively few amphibians and reptiles in Britain and Europe, compared with tropical parts of the world. But those few are well worth studying and some can be easily kept.

Amphibians, as their name implies, spend part of their lives in water, and part of it out on land. Commonest over much of Europe are the frogs and toads, familiar to everyone with their extremely powerful long back legs for hopping. Lizard-like in shape, but not related, are newts and salamanders, whose webbed feet and flattened tails indicate their abilities as swimmers. In Britain, some rare newts are protected by law and must not be touched.

Reptiles have a harder, drier skin than amphibians and (though many can and do swim) have no need to be close to water. They include the lizards, which are more numerous and more obvious in southern Europe and the snakes. The most common of these are the grass snake and adder, but remember the adder has a poisonous bite. **Watch** it, but **never** touch it. Snake-like, but actually a legless lizard, is the slow worm. All are cold-blooded, so are active only in the warmer summer months and during the heat of the day.

Most amphibians are commonly found in ponds or in damp shady places nearby. They can be kept in an aquarium which **must** have rocks emerging from the water. Lizards and snakes can be kept in a vivarium – a dry glass tank with sand, leaves and rocks at the bottom. Feed them on worms, flies, maggots and meal worms.

REPRODUCTION

Amphibians mate and lay their eggs in their home ponds. Frogs and toad "spawn" can be easily (but carefully) collected and its development watched in an aquarium. Most reptiles lay eggs, leaving them to hatch in sunny, sandy banks or deep in the warmth of a compost heap. In some, the egg hatches inside the mother, so live young are born.

salamander

lizard

newt

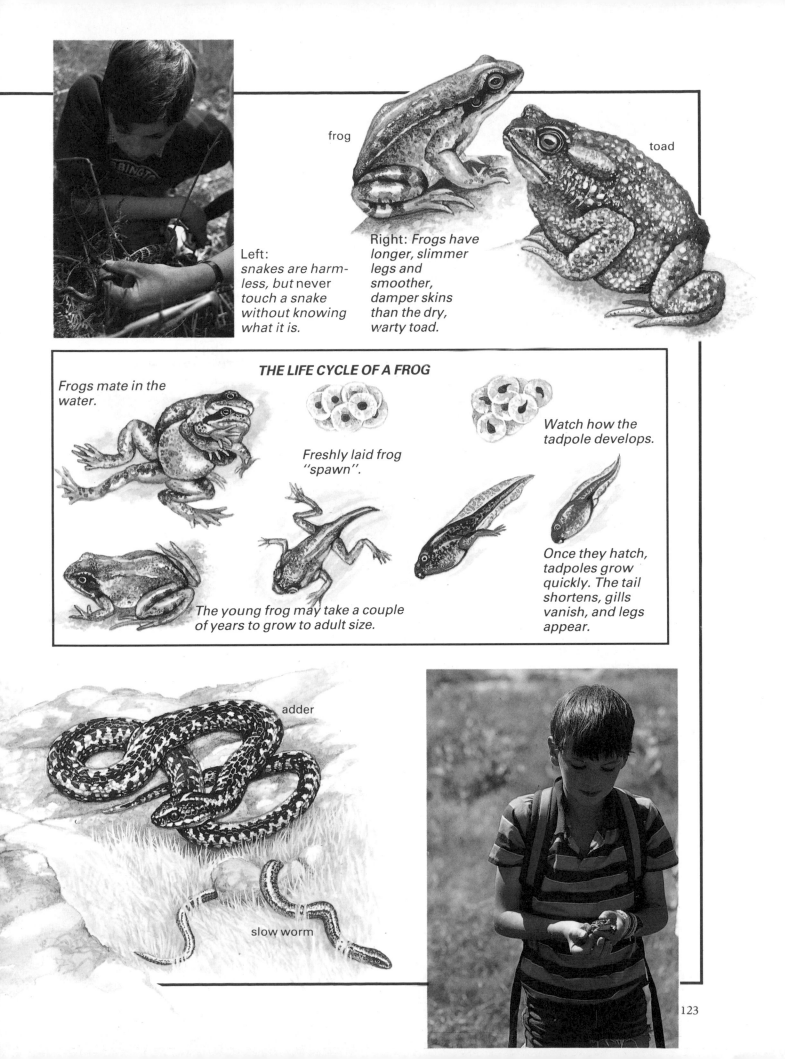

frog

toad

Left:
snakes are harmless, but never touch a snake without knowing what it is.

Right: *Frogs have longer, slimmer legs and smoother, damper skins than the dry, warty toad.*

THE LIFE CYCLE OF A FROG

Frogs mate in the water.

Freshly laid frog "spawn".

Watch how the tadpole develops.

Once they hatch, tadpoles grow quickly. The tail shortens, gills vanish, and legs appear.

The young frog may take a couple of years to grow to adult size.

adder

slow worm

123

KEEPING RECORDS

The notes that you make, and the sketches or photographs that you take on your nature watching expeditions, will be of great help to you as you get to know more about your subject. Just as important, many local or national natural history and conservation societies keep data banks of the occurrence and distribution of animals and plants. This information can be used to compile distribution maps: without the contributions of amateur naturalists like yourself, the distribution maps in field guides could never be produced.

A great deal of information – such as regular counts of birds at birdwatching spots – is used by local or national conservation bodies to defend our countryside from unwanted and ecologically harmful develop- ments. The people involved in this work have to be given regular, updated facts.

THE COUNTRY CODE
- √ guard against all risks of fire
- √ keep all gates closed
- √ keep dogs under proper control
- √ keep to the footpaths
- √ be careful not to damage hedges, fences or walls
- √ take your litter home
- √ safeguard water supplies
- √ protect all wildlife

Right: *If you come across a developing toadstool, go back and make notes of it as it grows. Your sketches will tell you a lot about the different stages of its life.*

Below: *A Polaroid camera provides you with an instant record of your observation.*

Foxglove (Digitalis purpurea)
Place: Mitcham Common
Date: 2nd June

Left and below: *From sketches in pencil and crayon in your notepad, draw and paint pictures for your records. Remember to note where and when you saw something.*

124

USING FIELD GUIDES

There are many good field guides on the market that are pocket-sized, reasonably cheap and accurate. Build up a collection of guides on those topics that particularly interest you – your accuracy of identification will improve and your interest in a fascinating hobby will increase even more. Make sure you have discovered how your guide is set out and that you have understood any identification keys it may use. In many guides it is not possible to show, for example, different species of insects – there may only be representatives of the major groups. Sometimes you may need more specialized guides.

Trying to photograph wildlife can be difficult, as it is hard to get close enough for a detailed shot. With a good deal of patience, you should get some fun results!

Left and above: *"Fast" colour films are available, but they give a grainy image for nature photography. It is better to use a slower film and an electronic flash, which helps to give a greater depth of focus and "stopping" movement.*

Right: *Most small plants, particularly parts of flowers, and small animals such as insects, can be studied much better through a good lens – ×10 magnification is ideal. Many cameras can take either extension rings or supplementary lenses to create a magnified "close-up" image.*

INDEX

DEAN
ALL-COLOUR
activity
BOOK